THE ELEPHANT AND THE BAOBAB

Like mine your skin is wrinkled by the sun.

When elephants rub themselves against the trunk of a baobab they must surely feel a sense of companionship with the tree. Its outer layer in so many ways resembles an elephant's skin: they're both lumpy and grey, and often covered in mud. With age the convoluted folds in the tree's main stem mirrors the legs of many elephant bulls standing together at a seep in the desert sand.

An Elephant Bloodline

First published by Rra-Thohoyandou Press in 2007

Text © Howard Blight 2007
Artwork as signed © Joanne Pohl 2006
Artwork as signed © Maggie Baleta 2006
Design and getup © Electric Book Works 2007

ISBN: 978-0-9584969-1-9

Production by Electric Book Works (www.electricbookworks.com)
Cover design by Toby Newsome (www.tobyjug.co.za)
Map and elephant-anatomy illustration by Anne Westoby
Small recurring elephant heads by Joanne Pohl
Set in Warnock Pro (story) and Chaparral Pro (notes)

E-mail: amoren@mweb.co.za

Visit the website at www.elephantbloodline.com, and the Elephants for Africa Forever website at www.efaf.co.za.

An elephant bloodline

Based on a true African story

Howard Blight
Phophoroga

With illustrations by
Joanne Pohl and Maggie Baleta

RRA-THOHOYANDOU
PRESS

Afterwards, one of us asked, 'What is the difference between us and the elephants?'

Many differences, as big as elephants, no doubt – yet we sat dumb a while, not sure what to answer.

Then one, the one who has devoted her life to elephants, said, 'The difference is that human beings are the only species that claims to be made in God's image.'

So, maybe God is an elephant. A large female somewhere out there on the plains, tossing dust onto her shoulders, surrounded by her disciples.

Maybe God has huge grey ears.

Maybe God's body is so massive that it seems to flow on its bones.

Maybe God's tusks are long, tapered arcs.

I've heard stranger claims.

Howard Nelson

To Diane and our daughters
Nikki, Claudie and Lolly

and to the elephants

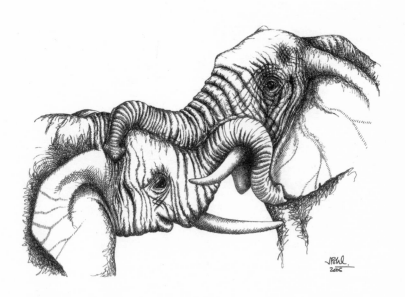

Contents

Foreword

Elephants are magnificent creatures that fascinate us. They are so huge that we tend to feel virtually powerless in their presence without powerful weapons to protect us. Nevertheless, these peaceful, gentle giants are vegetarians and not predators. We enjoy watching their family interactions, especially the playful, cute young ones. Their lifespan is similar to ours and their young need an extended upbringing, similar to human children. We are aware of their intelligence and long memories. We are deeply touched by their emotions, especially when they take care of their sick, and how they mourn their dead.

Many people encounter elephants in the safe space provided by conservation areas in the African wilderness. We often assume that those elephants have carefree lives and few natural enemies. Few people are aware of the many dangers and challenges elephants face from humans, their major enemy. Shrinking land available in which to roam freely, poaching for ivory, and culling to rid various southern African countries of an overpopulation of elephants are some of the causes of thousands of elephant deaths.

In this book Howard Blight combines his deep compassion for elephants, his extensive knowledge of the African savanna, and his strong concern for the well-being of a balanced biodiversity on the African continent to develop explanations portraying the complexities of elephant life in the twenty-first century. He carefully interweaves his own experience and current scientific knowledge about elephants into various narratives about different individual elephants. He introduces readers to different worlds where elephants face a variety of challenges: some exciting, others life-threatening.

The stories about the elephants are entertaining, but also aim to educate. In this book elephants are elephants, nothing more and nothing less. As far as it is possible for a human writing about animals, Howard does not portray elephants with human characteristics. Instead he shows us elephant life as our best scientific knowledge judges it to be. For this reason these elephant stories will give readers a much deeper insight into the joys and sorrows, the pleasures and pains, and the frustrations and satisfactions that elephants experience. The book will assist readers to imaginatively enter a world as experienced by elephants.

Hennie Lotter
Professor of Philosophy, University of Johannesburg
Chairperson, Ethics Society of South Africa, 2004–2006

Map

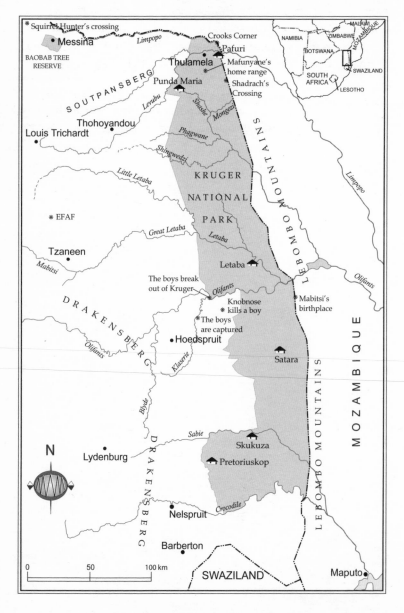

Elephant anatomy

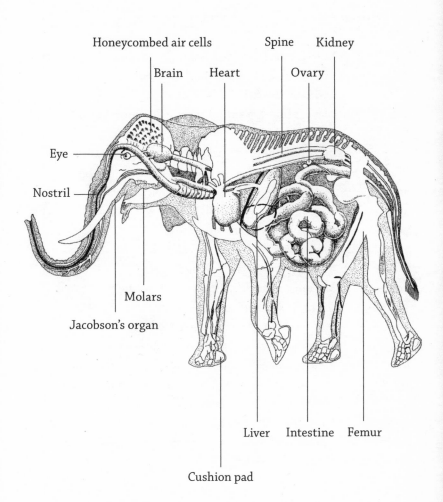

Honeycombed air cells

Brain   Heart

Spine   Kidney

Ovary

Eye

Nostril

Molars

Jacobson's organ

Cushion pad

Liver   Intestine   Femur

A timeline of
The Kruger National Park

Events in italics are assumed or fictionalised in this book.

1905	Stevenson Hamilton starts anti-poaching. There was no record of elephants in the area now known as The Kruger National Park.
1926	Magnificent-Seven bull Mafunyane born. Magnificent-Seven bull Shawu born. Act of Union parliament preserves the game sanctuary and names it the Kruger National Park.
1927	Magnificent-Seven bull Ndlulamithi born.
1934	Magnificent-Seven bull Shingwedzi born.
1935	Magnificent-Seven bull Dzombo born.
1930s–40s	Magnificent-Seven bull Kambaku born. Magnificent-Seven bull João born.
1960	*Mafunyane attacked aged 34, resulting in the hole in the top of his head.*
1966	*Mafunyane mates with cow-with-slight-limp's mother.*
1967	*Matriarch with slight limp born.* Culling begins in The Park. Population estimated at 6 586 elephants.
1968	*Mafunyane mates with Mabitsi's grandmother.*
1969	*Matriarch with tusk curving outwards born.*
1970	*Mabitsi's mother is born, the cow with the torn left ear.*
1972	*Shadrach kills cow with slight limp's aunt. The half-sisters are separated.*

1982	Shingwedzi dies.
1983	Mafunyane dies. Dzombo dies.
1984	*Tembo is born.*
1985	Ndlulamithi dies. Kambaku dies.
1986	*Tembo's family is culled. Tembo leaves Kruger and arrives at Tshukudu. Shawu dies.*
1988	*Klaserie is born.*
1989	*Letaba is born. Klaserie's mother is killed.*
1990	**MABITSI IS BORN.** *His mother is 20 years or 240 moons old.*
1991	*Limpopo is born.*
1993	*Trek to the Hill of Hope begins.*
1994	*Lord Rijhna retires from African duties.* Elephant-culling in Kruger is stopped.
1995	*Mabitsi returns to his birthplace.*
1996	*Mma-Thohoyandou, the elephant goddess, appointed.*
2000	João dies.
2001	*Knobnose kills a boy.*
2002	*The five young first-musth bulls join forces.*
2003	EFAF established. Tembo arrives at EFAF.
2004	*Knobnose is shot.* The remaining first-musth bulls arrive at EFAF.
2005	Tembo's twenty-first birthday.
2006	Six more elephants join EFAF.
2007	Estimated population of elephants in Kruger is 14 000. Three more elephants join EFAF. Minister Van Schalkwyk proposes a national elephant policy. Culling could be resumed.

The elephant bloodline

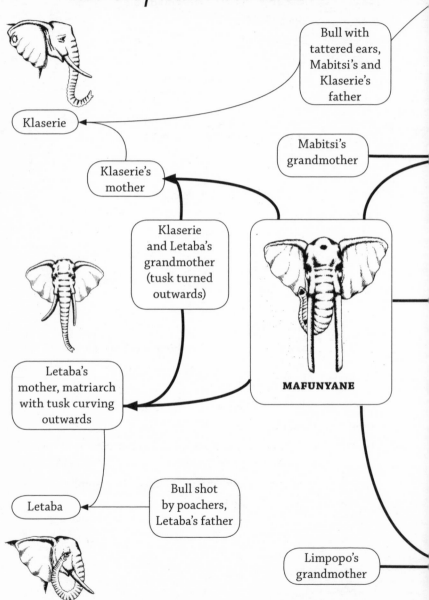

Bull with tattered ears, Mabitsi's and Klaserie's father

Klaserie

Mabitsi's grandmother

Klaserie's mother

Klaserie and Letaba's grandmother (tusk turned outwards)

MAFUNYANE

Letaba's mother, matriarch with tusk curving outwards

Bull shot by poachers, Letaba's father

Letaba

Limpopo's grandmother

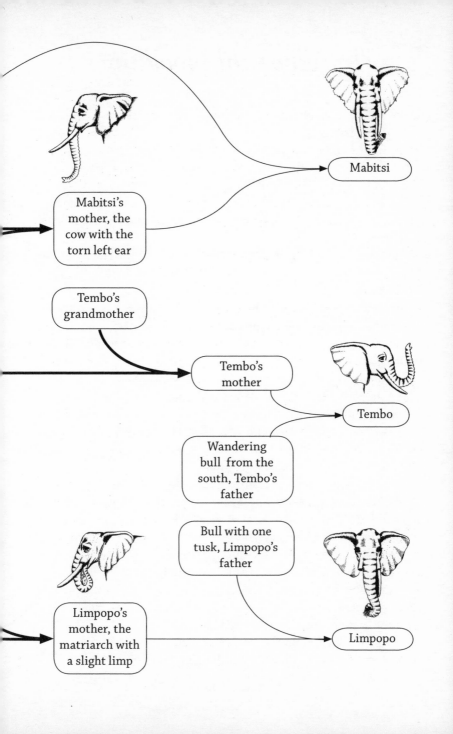

About this book

There are more elephants in southern Africa (Botswana, South Africa, Zimbabwe and Namibia) today than there have ever been. Their numbers are estimated at over 250 000.

The saving, capture, and training of Tembo, a partially habituated 19-year-old bull elephant, who broke out of his Tshukudu Game Reserve home in Limpopo Province, South Africa, in 2003 after having been seriously intimidated by wild bulls in musth, saw him come into the safe and gentle hands of the African Elephant Whisperers, Rory and Lindie Hensman. Mabitsi, Letaba, Limpopo and Klaserie joined Tembo at Elephants For Africa Forever (EFAF) in September 2003, prompting me to write this book. Knobnose had been shot and the lives of the four remaining bulls were being threatened.

I have speculated in the most sincere sense as to where, and under what circumstances, these adult elephants may have been born. Their respective births and other adventures in the fabric of the narrative are created from actual happenings with other elephants in the natural world.

I have tried to balance the real with the fantasy world, to enable readers of all ages to more fully comprehend the wonders and dilemmas of elephant family life.

With the exception of Lord Rijhna, the Asian god of the elephants and prosperity, and Mma-Thohoyandou (pronounced Toy-an-doe), the mythological African elephant goddess and the goddess of biodiversity and gender diversity – and further references to elephants and mice – this faction attempts to interpret the way elephant family life unfolds in their natural environment. I have researched and recorded how successfully elephants communicate with one another and other elephant families, and how intelligent they really are.

Let's give Lord Rijhna the licence that the narrative offers, so that when he hands over his custodianship of Africa's elephants to Mma-Thohoyandou (Mother with the Head of an Elephant), to help guide and assist Africa's people in their deliberations regarding elephants, it is accepted with the same empathy and understanding that the elephants feel for one another.

Mma-Thohoyandou is crying out for a sympathetic ear. Help her to help us to secure and preserve balanced biological wilderness sanctuaries for our children, as well as the elephants. The veld, the bush, and the riverine scrub should forever remain a home and refuge for the elephants to live in, and die next to, in peace, having lived their natural lifespan.

Enjoy this journey with me. Read, learn, and come away more fulfilled, with an understanding of the natural world here in southern Africa – in the same way, perhaps, that elephants perceive their environment. Mabitsi – and his extended family – offers us a window into their lives, as he embodies an elephant bloodline.

How the elephants were named

Mabitsi, Letaba, Limpopo and Klaserie were named when they came to EFAF, who saved them from being shot. The first to be darted, in the lowveld near Kruger, was a young bull whose age was estimated at thirteen years. The perennial Mabitsi River runs through a section of pristine subtropical rain forest near Tzaneen in South Africa's Limpopo Province. To record these early days of Elephants for Africa Forever (EFAF), the first wild elephant was named Mabitsi.

The second elephant had to be named Letaba. This is the major river which carves its way through the countryside near to what would be the elephants' new home. (The Mabitsi River is, in fact, a tributary of the Letaba River, which flows into the Olifants and eventually on into the Limpopo, which reaches the Indian Ocean at Xia Xia in Mozambique.)

In acknowledgement of the enormous encouragement and assistance given to EFAF by the provincial authorities, we named the third elephant Limpopo. His age was estimated at fifteen years or one hundred and eighty moons.

The capture of all four elephants had taken place near the town of Hoedspruit to the south-east of the confluence of the Blyde and Olifants Rivers in the Limpopo Province, and the other prominent watercourse in the area is the Klaserie River. There is also the Klaserie Dam, which facilitates a permanent stream for primary water use and game alike throughout the year. And so the last elephant to be darted – and the oldest, at 17 – was named Klaserie.

Elephant time and elephant age

There are twelve moons in one year, and perhaps elephants recognise this way of marking time. In the story, elephant time is measured from one full moon to the next.

The number of teeth or molars elephants use during their lifetime establishes their age. Elephants have six large sets of molars. The huge molars are manufactured from the calcium in their jawbones as they grow. As they masticate these molars wear away, while at the same time migrating forward in the jawbone and being replaced from behind. At age three, the elephant gets its second molar, at six its third, at sixteen its fourth. By the time the elephant is twenty-seven the fifth molar has emerged, and at forty-two the final molar arrives. Once this last molar has worn away, the animal generally dies of malnutrition between the ages of fifty-five and sixty, depending on its diet. Because they are unable to masticate food containing a balanced, nutritional diet, an elephant may die of malnutrition rather than starvation. Soft grasses are not able to satisfy an elephant's nutritional needs.

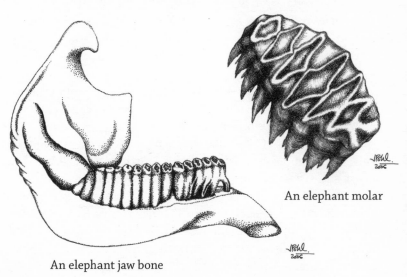

An elephant molar

An elephant jaw bone

Elephant communication

'It is said that elephants talk to one another, mumbling with their mouths the speech of men, but not all the speech of beasts is audible, but only the men who tame them hear it.'

Oppian, *Cynegetica*

In the mid 1980s Kate Payne joined Joyce Poole in Kenya to participate in the remarkable research Joyce had initiated to record and define – if possible, an elephant language.

To date, no specific elephant words or language has been identified, yet we do retain a substantial understanding of how elephants communicate with one another, at what frequencies they talk to each other and under what behavioural circumstances they produce sound levels below the level of human hearing. These are known as infrasound. Low frequency sounds and other vocalisations inaudible to the human ear are also produced by elephants.

It has been established that most rumbles, screams and trumpets made by Savanna elephants contain fundamental frequencies between 14 and 30 hertz and are rich in infrasound. Certain sound pressure levels are as high as 102 decibels, measured at close quarters. For some comparison, a heavy, noisy truck at 15 metres emits 90 decibels.

So thorough was Joyce Poole's research that she compiled a list of calls. Many of these calls have been observed at close quarters by other people working with elephants.

During periods of sexual excitement, and more particularly with females in oestrus and males in musth, certain distinctive recognisable vocalisations were recorded. The oestrus rumble is regularly used by females to inform bull elephants of their condition and willingness to mate. The remarkable female chorus often produced by numerous females can be heard as a response to a musth rumble. During genital testing certain low frequency, almost inaudible, rumbles are produced in acknowledgement of oestrus.

When elephants express social excitement they accompany much of their vocalisations with recognisable body movements. When individuals or groups of elephants meet, they produce a greeting rumble. Social rumbles are produced when a herd or family meets. Elephants roar when identifying one another or as a confidence builder.

Often during mating, a pandemonium rumble or chorus is expressed.

Elephants love to play. They chase one another and splash and roll against each other during bathing and mock charges. During these demonstrations of their friendship they often produce play trumpets. This contrasts with the social trumpet, which can also demonstrate disappointment.

During times of distress, females in particular produce reassurance rumbles. Calves produce a calf response. Calves regularly produce a suckle-distress scream when they wish to nurse. And quite naturally, calves often offer a fear trumpet in times of anxiety. This differs from a distress call and a suckle rumble or a suckle cry.

Elephants remain highly social and gregarious animals. When young bull elephants first come into musth at the age of thirteen or fourteen, they leave the security of the family groups. These bulls form bachelor herds. Some of these younger bulls often link up with older more experienced bulls. These older bulls welcome the company of these younger bulls or askaris, who synergistically learn the trade of what it requires to be a dominant bull elephant with greater hierarchical status.

But the dominating force in elephant society remains the breeding herds, run and fostered by the matriarchal system. Dominant, experienced elephant cows become Matriarchs in their own herds. These cows retain the knowledge to guide and advise the family group.

The whole focus within these breeding herds is on the calves. They remain reliant on their mothers until they are seven or eight years old. On the occasions when these herds are under threat, from whatever source, elephants produce attack rumbles.

Sub-adult elephants become independent at the age of eight and retain almost no hierarchical status in the herd until sexual maturity at fourteen to fifteen years.

The necessity for efficient communications within these breeding herds has resulted in the development of numerous other contact vocalisations.

The Let's go rumble, requesting the herd to move along, and the contact call, are used to say, *Where are you? We are here!* Correspondingly, the contact answer denotes, in elephant, *Okay, we are here and coming.*

Also frequently used in the breeding herds are the coalition rumble and the discussion rumble, informing the elephants to gather around.

There are specific sounds used to indicate fear and surprise when strangers arrive. The trumpet blast and snort are infrasound noises but specific infrasound alarms are used to impress these feelings on the rest of the herd.

For social fear warnings, the scream, bellow and groan are frequently used to alert the herd.

Perhaps one of the most commonly used ranges of vocalisations is to indicate dominance. There is the female-to-female call, the musth rumble that is used to flush out cows in oestrus, and the male-to-male calls used predominantly by bachelors.

The journey

Sit around a camp-fire in the African bush for long enough of an evening and sooner or later the 'elephant debate' surfaces; along with those other perennials, malaria and snakebite treatment. As elephants feature strongly in this book, I am throwing myself on the reader's indulgence to put forward my small case for The Elephant.

Keith Meddows, author of Sand in the wind *and* Sometimes when it rains, *Hwange, August 1997*

Prologue

In the beginning of elephant time, there were one hundred-and-twenty moons (ten human years) when no rainfall of any significance had fallen in the area that is now the renowned Kruger National Park. The wilderness as it is recognised today had collapsed. The grass had shrivelled, and except for a few shrubs and reeds growing along the banks of the larger rivers, there remained no sustainable browse or grazing on the southern African bushveld.

The Kalahari desert to the north was also void of any visible life. On scalding summer days dust eddies soared like tornadoes in the dry African sky, where only the vultures remained, kept aloft by the updrafts they flew so well. The last tree that grew in a forest of baobabs had shrunk, died and disintegrated. The remains of its once huge, truncated, fibrous stem and fat, lumpy branches, lay strewn across the hills to the west of the Phugwane River. All that was left was the putrid smell of fermenting organic matter. Most of the plains game had migrated to the south of the open veld, leaving it empty, barren and silent. Only the scavengers remained, picking through the remnants of a once beautiful and balanced landscape.

On the extremity of the scattered, decaying branches of the once-mighty baobab was the stump of a previously green and shady marula tree. Over many previous moons, the marula tree had yielded tons of refreshingly sweet, bright-yellow fruit, which attracted the elephants for regular gatherings. Now the tree, its fruit and the comforting shade that it once offered, were all gone, with only its stump protruding from the earth. Between the two tree-skeletons lay a slab of black dolerite rock, looking like a partially buried old elephant bull. He lay as if in humble submission to the devastation that Lord Rijhna observed in the region.

This god of the elephants and of prosperity had the head of an elephant and the body of a man – and thus a foot in both worlds. He thought that perhaps it was time for a new beginning. He had been appointed as the custodian of all the elephants in the world, at a time lost even to elephant memory. He sat and watched.

Astride the rock elephant sat an arrogant, male Chacma Baboon. He posed as though he'd earned a seat in the animal parliament. This statesman was the head of a troop of fifty-seven other baboons and demanded attention. He had discovered the last uneaten fruit shed by the baobab and hammered the ovoid, golden, velvety-haired shell onto the smooth surface of the black rock where he sat. He busied himself with the crop of seeds that the pod contained. Embedded in the dry, bittersweet cream-of-tartar powder, were small kidney-shaped beans. He dissolved the tasty compact powder crusted around the seeds, relishing the flavour. He nibbled every last morsel coating the seeds.

He was highly regarded by all who knew him. The baboon allowed the shiny seeds to slip from the side of his mouth, dropping them onto the sand.

He yawned; his jaws threateningly agape. He exposed his gums while flaunting his sharp white teeth as a warning for any challenger to his authority.

The seeds scattered and came to rest, camouflaged amongst chips that had flaked off the dolerite rock.

A striped field mouse darted forward and picked up three of the seeds, packing them into the storage pockets on each side of her furry mouth. She rushed back into her burrow without looking up. A yellowy-brown ground squirrel moved nervously from between the fibrous branches of the baobab. The tiny animal's long, bushy tail flicked nervously as he searched for a few of the seeds. The squirrel picked up one seed with both front paws and sat upright, using his tail to balance his body. He nibbled ferociously at the hard crust, eventually revealing the nutritious, white pith of the small embryo; he concentrated hard.

The dark-grey, male baboon watched, intelligent and curious.

Standing not far off, having remained motionless and silent, disguised as he was against the sandy desert floor, stood a short, sinewy man. His skin was yellowy amber and he was clad only in a leather loincloth, with a genet's tail dangling between his naked buttocks. His face seemed moulded from clay and his eyes were narrow

slits in the crevices of his sun-baked cheeks. The little figure had observed this scene unfold many times, and required only one ally: patience. He balanced on feet that were broad at the front, with the toes spread in the shape of a fan. He had smeared his torso and crotch with baboon droppings to camouflage his strong human odour.

Between his teeth the San clansman held the carved bone-tip of a tiny missile. By lowering his head, he inserted this arrowhead onto a reed-shaft notched against the taut string of a bow held between his outstretched hands.

The baboon and the man lived in the same neighbourhood, respecting one another's space. The old male baboon regarded the man and his nomadic family dismissively.

As the squirrel licked at the baobab seed, the hunter lifted his weapon as though his arms were swept upwards by a soft breeze. With the accuracy honed throughout his life, he released the thin, featherless arrow. Its flight was short and silent. The sharp bone arrowhead sliced deeply into the squirrel's rib-cage, cutting through the small animal's body and embedding itself in the rotting tree stump. The victim uttered a series of clicks and rattles, like dry seed pods on a winter's day. He squealed aloud only once and then shivered as though struck by a blast of cold air. Then he lay quite still.

The man darted forward to retrieve his prize.

The big baboon moved away, respectfully turning his head while nervously lifting his eyebrows repeatedly to reveal his hazel eyes.

A Spotted Dikkop announced his part in this wilderness theatre and applauded, piping, *You clever, clever, clever old thing.*

As the man gathered up his quarry, he also recognised and retrieved several of the baobab seeds which lay scattered where he stood. He placed them in a pouch made from the dried and salted scrotum of a kudu bull. He would roast and grind the seeds into a fine powder, and when he next visited the hot springs to the north, he would pour the black powder into an empty ostrich eggshell. When the steaming water was added, he knew it would serve up a tasty beverage which would gain him favour with a girl in the band. He smiled and relished the thought.

As the slender figure busied himself with his primitive duties, his right foot shuffled one of the baobab seeds sideways and it slid into a crevice in the soil between the rock and the tree stump. The seed rolled into the darkness of the narrow opening, coming to rest a forearm's length from the surface. As the man turned to move away, his heel inadvertently pressed against the soft, dry earth. And there it would lie, fertile and secure.

As the squirrel hunter moved away he noticed a number of flat, slightly rounded, sharpened rock chips that had cracked off the outer surface of the boulder. Variations in day and night temperatures had caused the rock to expand and contract. He rummaged through these natural skinning tools, selecting only two. Holding them in the clenched fist of his left hand, he moved away from the scene of death, running off to join other members of his band with his squirrel prize.

He jogged at a steady pace for two hours, having dis-
embowelled the tiny animal. As he ran he reflected on the
bean-shaped baobab seeds and the hot drink he intended to
prepare. He planned to collect a ball of dry elephant dung,
the smoke from which, when lit, would subdue the attacks
of the bees from whom he intended to steal some honey to
sweeten the tasty beverage. All aspects of life amused and
delighted him.

The San hunter joined the other members of his family
on his homeward journey. The band was conscious of the
devastation which surrounded them. At the first full moon
following the frugal squirrel hunt, the leaders of the family,
the senior councillors and the shamans, knew that it was time
to once again perform the ceremony of the rain dance.

They draped themselves with simple, ancient adornments
and sipped the juice of a ground melon, or rumputis,
collected from a stretch of alluvial soil. They created illusions
of cloud cover and moist air. They wished for the swelling

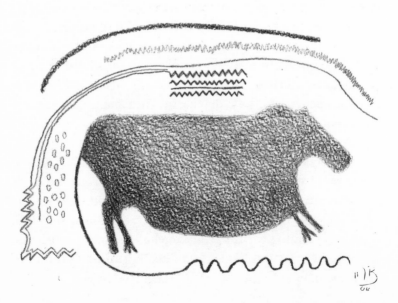

and darkening of the puffs of clouds in the heavens. Their own rain gods, in the shape of four-legged beasts, emerged. These gentle monsters danced in the sky and bounced off the earth in celebration. Their shape-shifting took them into the body of a black eland bull, his dewlap waving rhythmically under his neck and onto his chest. The whole band cavorted throughout the night, weaving into and across the flames of a central wood fire to the east of their sleeping quarters, and to the north of the Southern Cross, positioned so clearly in the night sky.

Utterly exhausted, the !Kung Bushmen came to rest one by one, collapsing where they danced.

Some moons later, on an evening following another burning day, the clouds gathered against the escarpment. They rumbled and rolled in excited confusion, cracking and dancing in slow motion, thundering into one another and releasing streaks of yellow and white lights, illuminating the heavens.

The mass of cloud bands tumbled and moved back and away from the mountains, releasing icy winds that collided with the dry soil and boiled up a dust storm that blinded the landscape.

Then there was an extended moment of silence following one final gigantic thunder clap, as large, single drops of rain descended towards the dust bowl. The droplets were warm and inviting and as each one hit the earth, minute moon-craters pockmarked the dust. Lord Rijhna folded his arms and smiled.

Following the first few drops, there was a deluge rarely encountered in the region. Most animals had never experienced such a cataclysm and ran around confused, seeking refuge while the rain pounded the earth and soaked the soil, rushing into the cracks in the clay and filling the sandy crevices with muddy water.

The baobab seed slept on through the first wave of the storm, where it had lain undisturbed for the last thirty-nine moons. For four moons the deep empty fissures in underground canyons were slowly replenished. Depressions created by long periods of elephant mud-bathing were filled with rainwater. The downpour slowed to a steady, soaking, windless torrent.

The floodwaters rose and rushed past the dolerite rock. The marula stump stood fast. The water roared over the sharp edges of the black rock, ripping slabs from its flank. The fibrous branches of the decaying baobab were rolled together like heavy tangles of rope. These cables swept all before them as they lassoed and cleared the riverbanks. The striped field mouse was washed from her burrow and bobbed like a buoy on the surface of the tide.

African Bullfrogs which had lain in wait below the dry pans hibernating in the earth since the previous rains, all those moons ago, emerged in their thousands. They popped their heads above the surface of the water and produced a series of low-pitched yaps. They were ready to breed.

Brown-backed Tree Frogs climbed down from their roosts, sounding off at intervals with low two-syllabled quacks. Terrestrial Bushveld Rain-frogs emerged, and produced short whistles. Colourful Red-legged Kassinas blurted incessant quackings. The bubbling kassinas offered clear, modulated quoits. White Foam-nest Frogs constructed nests overhanging the pans and then sat back to compose their own croaks and squeaks. There were ornate frogs, dwarf and snoring puddle-frogs, and mottled shovel-nosed frogs – all offering their own personalised vocal gratitude for the rains after so many moons of patience. The brown seed slept on through the downpour and the sounds of the orchestra. But the soil in the drenched grave where the seed lay had pressured tiny molecules of water beneath and into the hard testa protecting the fertile, patient embryo, deep within its protective outer coating.

The first signs of life stirred in the belly of the seed.

After another two moons of incessant rain, the seed was swollen, saturating the white expectant interior with its high protein, starch and minerals. The embryo cracked the dark outer layer of the seed. First, a thin, creamy root emerged. It moved down through the soil, securing the seed's position. Once the root had established an anchorage, a tiny, pale shoot appeared, growing upwards in search of daylight.

The rains ceased and the level of the floodwaters receded. The young baobab seedling pushed its way through the surface of the soil, where it was greeted by quite a different landscape to the one it had left all those moons ago. Seeds of every description, dormant for so long, had burst into life. The sun emerged, warming and nourishing the soil and the seedlings. A light breeze blew, helping to unfold leaves and open flowers to create a new, green carpet in the wilderness. A more generous magic could not be conceived.

The baobab seedling surged ahead over many moons, bearing upwards, branching and establishing itself as a landmark on the veld near the Phugwane River. Over time it grew into an enormous tree, experiencing variable seasons and growing lumpy with age as it matured, harbouring untold secrets and showing nothing except its strength. But the elephants in every generation were informed, through the deep, knowing rumbles offered by their parents and the matriarchs of the various herds as they passed, that when this tree had germinated, it was In The Beginning.

Even now, as elephant herds pass the baobab and scratch their muddy, leathery skins against a slab of black dolerite next to the tree, they must wonder why it is there. It is strangely shaped, as part of the exposed rock resembles the hindquarters of someone they all think they recognise. On many occasions when elephants have gathered under the tree, a gaunt, yellow figure, secure in his hiding place, is said to appear from between the branches and gaze down at them. There is always the crease of a smile that appears around his coppery mouth. Some of the elephants occasionally lift their heads and trumpet at the lean figure high in the canopy of the baobab, in what can only be celebration.

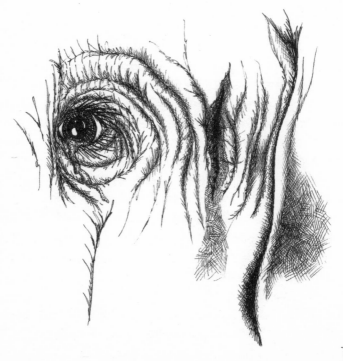

1

To hunt an elephant

18 years or 216 moons prior to the birth of Mabitsi

Shadrach was dreaming of ivory; a stepping stone to millet beer, plump women, laughter and frolicsome song. He stirred and shifted his weight on the reed mat where he slept. His head was supported on a wooden pillow, a *xiseketelo xa nonga*. The nonga prevented insects and scorpions from crawling into his ears at night when he lay fully prostrate on the ground.

Shadrach was a Shangaan from Chief Murumbini's tribal area. He hunted elephants and rhinoceros for a living. He was reared from a strong Shangaan (Tsonga) lineage of the finest trackers and marksmen. They were the best elephant poachers on the continent, second only to the Wata from East Africa.

But Shadrach was in a league of his own. He was born in the 1930s, but no one knew when and where for certain. Shadrach had served his apprenticeship as a poacher in the Gona re

Zhou National Park in southern Rhodesia, which would soon be Zimbabwe. He was reported to have shot their famous big tusker, Kambanji. The anti-poaching squads of the time had hounded him out of the area, whereupon he disappeared.

Shadrach's hallmark in his early years was his deadly use of a .375 magnum Holland and Holland double rifle. He had stolen it from a farmhouse in the Chiredzi district in southern Rhodesia. Later he used whatever military calibres were available – AK 47s, FNs and M16s.

Lying touching Shadrach's lean naked chest and stomach now was his rifle, one of the deadliest hunting weapons in existence. Shadrach was a head shot specialist, fearless enough to approach elephants on foot, up close. He had cleaned and polished his rifle, once more returning it to its oily, muslin-lined case. The gun case had been lovingly fashioned from the tanned skin of a wildebeest bull he had shot when he was in his teens. Regular use and oiling had turned the leather dark with age and soft and pliable. The black hunter moved again in his sleep, returning once more to snore rhythmically as he dreamed of the forthcoming adventure.

A hyena moved in the distance, calling a series of low drawn-out *Wooop, wooop, wooops*. This was followed by the cackles of a lone black-backed jackal: together they haunted the night.

The hunting party of twelve was securely camped out some twenty kilometres north of the Mozambique town of Mapai, on the banks of the Rio Lilau in a forest of niandoubos. While travelling west, they had crossed the railway after dark and were asleep by one a.m.

The poachers woke at four-fifteen, as a gregarious flock of community-minded red-billed buffalo weavers announced the dawn with a chorus of songs and chortles, mumbling *Be cheery, cheery, cheery, cheery.*

There was no bushfire smoke to blow the sleep from their eyes. Water, some dried meat and half a handful of sugar sent them on their way. The hunting party moved at ease through the knobthorn bush. When they saw the Kruger National Park fence some four hundred metres ahead, they slowed down on the pace, to put into practice their own anti-tracking procedures.

On a previous hunting trip, one of Shadrach's scouts had trapped and killed a kudu cow. The gang had removed the two front hooves by severing the legs just below the shin. The legs, with the skin still attached, were dried in winter sunshine. The entire hoof, skin, bone and sinew had been soaked in a strong brine solution to assist in its preservation. The now dehydrated tool offered maximum grip for the task at hand.

As the poachers walked towards the fence, they deliberately brushed their own footprints away with branches cut and bound from a magic guarri shrub. The feathery leaves made the perfect broom. The last man in the group pressed the kudu hooves onto the sandy soil at just the correct pressure, to replicate the spoor of antelope walking towards the fence.

By throwing two of their sleeping blankets over the fence, the gang members neutralised the eight thousand volts that energised the steel wires on the offset brackets. The group scaled the two-metre high electrified game fence. There were some sparks, but they were soon over, unscathed. They continued their diligent anti-tracking by leaving four deep indentations in the place where the kudu would have

landed, having cleared the fence with one gigantic leap – as they so often do.

The poachers moved on into The Park and climbed a mound of boulders.

They had entered just south of Crook's Corner, at Baobab Hill, and then stopped. Crook's Corner is in the northern Pafuri region of The Kruger National Park, where the borders of Zimbabwe and Mozambique join to meet South Africa. Generations of traders, and poachers and criminals fleeing the law, had used this secret outpost of forgotten wilderness, as a transitional refuge and corridor to apparent freedom. The poachers rested for a while and listened intently. The wilderness was silent, save for birdsong and the whisper of the breeze.

Without a word, Shadrach signalled to move on. They travelled south for three hours, parallel to the fence, until they encountered the first massive pylon carrying the overhead electric cables from the Cabora Bassa hydroelectric power plant on the Zambezi River, some nine hundred-and-twenty kilometres to the north. To the north in Mozambique, hundreds of pylons had been sabotaged during the bush war and the overhead aluminium cables carried no power. After scaling the pylon, Shadrach positioned himself comfortably and scanned the area with his 8 x 15 Zeiss binoculars. Evening was drawing in and his lean buttocks balanced him on the thick cables that spanned between the pylons.

He spotted a grey mass moving through the bush. *Tindlopfu*. Elephants. From high on his perch he signalled with his hands on either side of his head.

Shadrach carried a pale, earth-coloured calabash. The gourd had a fist-sized hole neatly removed from its bulbous body to create an instrument. At the handle-end, a broad bamboo mouthpiece had been inserted and secured with beeswax. By blowing firmly on this vegetable voice box, Shadrach had become skilled at mimicking the base sound of a bull elephant in musth. The musician rested a while and then took a deep breath and blew firmly and continuously. From the calabash came a musth rumble, alternated with a groan and a series of guttural tones; they resonated in the atmosphere. The sound filled the air, rising to meet the inversion layer in the night sky, where they were redirected and returned to the Earth, echoing off into the distance. He then clasped the gourd to his ear and, by cupping his hands around it, he listened with his eyes tightly closed. The mimic held this position for three minutes and then a crease appeared on either sides of his mouth. His eyes opened and twinkled with anticipation. He whispered *'Vavasati, va swi lava.'* The wives, they want it.

Some two hours' walk from where Shadrach sat, an elephant cow in oestrus had picked up the sounds of the musth rumble from this strange bull elephant. She could not resist answering the call with her own: *I'm out here.* To the north of where Shadrach roosted, there was another musth rumble from a competitive bull.

The hunter climbed down and announced, 'Hi etlela sweswi na kona hi ta tlota mundzuku.' We sleep now and hunt tomorrow.

The poachers were woken at midnight by torrential rain. For two days the storm scoured the landscape, bringing streams and rivers into instant flood. Torrents of water eroded the river banks, turning the floodwaters into a red soapy onslaught. This would be Shadrach's best chance under the cover of the rain and the darkness. No patrols would be out, no rifle shots would be heard.

'Tana i nkhari!' Come. It is time!

The hunting party moved in.

Forty-seven moons previously, the future Matriarch – the cow with the slight limp – had been born. Eighteen moons later she was blessed with a half-sister and the two young calves had grown up together, proudly carrying the genes of their father, the great and feared elephant bull, Mafunyane, in their bloodline.

On that terrible night as the floodwaters of the Mongezi River rose, the small herd of elephants, whose number included the two half-sisters, sheltered against the storm near the river bank in the lee of a hill.

Shadrach and his scouts approached from the north. The rain was driving and incessant, drenching the hunters to the skin. The water poured off them, down their legs, through their rubber shoes and into tiny tributaries, carrying tell-tale signs to the swollen river.

Suddenly the Matriarch lifted her trunk into the night sky and faced into the wind. She opened her ears. The tip of her truck touched the Jacobson's organ on her upper palate. There was danger in the air! She could smell the musty, sometimes putrid, odour of unwashed human skin.

It was time to go. She issued an urgent, *Let's go!* rumble as the first sign of dawn offered some vision for the young calves.

But she had held on for too long.

As the herd moved towards the flooded river, in the hope of heading downstream along its bank, there was a thunderous blast out of the driving rain. A shot had been fired.

Shadrach was acutely aware of the back-up safety implications of hunting elephants with a double-barrelled rifle. He was well versed with the technical attributes of the calibre .375, which gave the knock-out value of this rifle more than forty points. Through years of experience, Shadrach now used round-nosed, solid, 300 grain slugs. The bullet was set in front of a magnum, flanged, brass cartridge case, with fifty-eight grains of smokeless powder. It would deliver seventeen tons of knock-down pressure, with a muzzle velocity of 2 450 feet per second and a muzzle energy of over 4 000 foot pounds. In the right hands the calibre was efficient, the bullet, deadly.

It drove into a mature cow standing to the Matriarch's immediate left. The full-metal-jacket bullet entered the cow's head, a short distance in front of her ear opening. It bored into and through the honeycombed cavities of the elephant's skull, coming to rest in the first third of her large, grey brain. The animal lurched backwards onto her hind legs; her trunk was thrown back and over her head. She rocked forwards and collapsed, dead on her knees. Her trunk thrashed, beating a swathe through the high riverine grass as it came to rest. The ground reverberated under its impact, and mud cascaded up and into the rain.

Within an hour the smallish tusks were hacked out of the head of the slain cow. Shadrach moved north to bury his booty. 'Swi chelele e thlelo ka ribye. Hi ta vuya.' Bury them next to this rock. We will return later.

As his trackers moved east in single file along an elephant path, Shadrach turned to view the killing-fields. He lifted his chin and his chest was filled with pride and satisfaction. He thought to himself, 'Hi rhandza ndhawu leyi!' I like this place!

Terrified at the sound of gunfire, the calves followed their mothers as they plunged headlong into the swollen river, and were instantly swept away.

The two half-sisters were separated in the turbulence of the rushing waters.

The older calf, with her front foot trapped under a fallen log, screamed with pain while struggling against the river. The floodwaters swept over her head as she caught a last wide-eyed glimpse of her half-sister and her distinctive tusk that curved outwards. The younger calf held her trunk high above her head as the waters increased the distance that separated them. Absolute fear and loneliness replaced the peace and tranquillity that had dominated the family life of the elephants not half an hour before. The calf with the outward-curving tusk bobbed away on the floodwaters in the pale rain-soaked morning light, her fear coming to the younger calf on the air as she turned and struggled to release her own trapped foot.

With her head under the water, she pushed her tiny left tusk between the log and her footpad. The tusk slipped and entered the footpad between the two front toe nails, inflicting a pain so severe that she arched her back in agony. The effort wrenched her foot from under the fallen log and launched her into the main stream of the floodwaters, where she was bounced against the rocks and sandy river bed, her foot bleeding profusely.

At a turn in the river the calf was swept onto the stony river bank, where she lay exhausted between the roots and branches of dead and abandoned ana trees. She disentangled herself slowly from the mass of driftwood on the river bank and emerged, afraid and disorientated.

She strolled aimlessly through the mist and drizzle, eventually stumbling into a passing herd. She was instantly accepted and offered protection by her new family. Over the following days her foot developed a suppurating abscess. It swelled as the temperature of the flesh rose over forty-three degrees centigrade. The nail peeled off and when the swollen, necrotic toe eventually burst, yellowy pus oozed for four days, leaving the small foot bones exposed through the raw flesh.

The abscess took three weeks to heal. The wound would eventually close, leaving the footpad partially deformed and causing the young female calf to limp slightly as she tried to take the pressure off the affected limb. She never quite recovered.

The prolonged agony of her predicament had temporarily distracted her from the memory of the panicked screams of her half-sister, who had been washed downstream while she herself was trapped.

Where was she now?

Having been washed out of rushing water, the younger calf with the outward-curving tusk had walked along aimlessly in the rain for three days. She was eventually rescued by a large breeding herd feeding in a dense grove of mopani scrub. Many of the cows had argued and squabbled as to who would take custody of the new arrival, one of the mothers eventually agreeing to adopt the calf, who was weak, exhausted and near death.

The calf grew and familiarised herself with her new family, only breaking away years later to take up her own matriarchal duties in a separate area of The Park.

But the limping calf would never know this. She could not forget the pleading tones and resonances of her half-sister, even as their two herds followed their separate fortunes. Those fearful vibrations would remain firmly fixed in her mind.

2

Mafunyane's legacy

26 years or 312 moons prior to the birth of Mabitsi

Mafunyane was in his four hundred-and-eightieth moon. He was in his prime, one of the magnificent seven big tuskers of the Kruger National Park. He occupied the upper reaches of the Shingwedzi River and ranged between there and the Bububu Stream. This was one of the remotest areas in the north of The Park. Mafunyane was shy and avoided any contact with the ground staff of The Park, moving away discreetly whenever vehicles were in the vicinity. He had a hole recessed in the top of his head, which reached down into the nasal cavity. The aggravation resulting from this no doubt contributed to his name, which, translated from Tsonga was, 'the irritable one.' The hole in Mafunyane's head tapered inwards, and it is thought it was inflicted while he was dueling during a period of musth, in his boisterous, adolescent youth. More virile, yet not so Herculean.

A larger, stronger bull had taken up Mafunyane's musthy, testosterone-laden challenge and during the bout had inserted one of his tusks into the top of the younger animal's head. The offending tusk had penetrated deep into his honeycombed skull and the wound had taken many moons to heal.

On hot, dry days, the dusty air entered the cavity and irritated and demoralised the great bull elephant.

On the lapse of nine moons and for a period of three moons, something potent occurs in the life of mature elephant bulls. On this occasion the time was drawing near for Mafunyane. He was about to come into musth.

It began on a fresh autumn morning. The bull had been resting undisturbed beneath the shady canopy of a sycamore fig. The tree had an enormous stem covered with pale-brown to yellowish-brown papery bark. Within its dense canopy, the tree bore an abundance of fruit, which nestled in closely packed clusters on its many branches, offering food and sanctuary to numerous birds.

The bull was woken to the sounds of the Purple Crested Lourie, singing his joyous melody, rising to a highly pitched crescendo of, *Gallop along, gallop along, gallop along.* Mafunyane generally woke feeling rather grumpy. On this day things were particularly bad, as his temporal glands had swollen overnight and his penis was slightly extended. As he moved away from the security of the tree, two Blackcollared Barbets launched themselves into a duet: *What a bother, what a bother, what a bother.* Mafunyane reached up into the tree's lower branches and tore down a few trunk fulls of round, sweet, reddish figs.

As the great bull walked out into the open, one of his attending askaris followed him at a distance: he had consciously acknowledged the change in his masters' mood and condition: this bull was not to be trifled with.

Mafunyane stood for a moment, resting his head on his thick creamy-coloured tusks, which reached all the way to the ground. He was an impressive sight on any day. His ears flapped rhythmically against his head. Two drops of temporal-gland liquid fell from his cheek. He shook his leathery head, irritated by the flies around his eyes.

The tips of his tusks were chisel-shaped, worn so from his stance. The bull lifted his head and held his trunk up into the warm air and released a deep, guttural sound-pulsation; a musth rumble. The upper front section of his angular, grey head vibrated visibly, and then he froze, standing quite still. With his ears spread wide, he listened for a response. There was nothing, not even in the distance. The airwaves were mute. Only the chatter of the fruit-eating birds broke the silence. A dust eddy swirled under the huge bull's feet, engulfing him in a tornado of leaves and dry grass fronds.

Mafunyane moved off at a pace. He produced a dominance rumble: he was on a mission.

As he moved away, testosterone-contaminated urine dribbled from his large extended penis. It would leave an identification trail wherever he walked. This bull meant business. The seven more diminutive bulls, which accompanied him everywhere, noticed that Mafunyane's posture had changed. He seemed to be holding his head high when he walked. His legs seemed to have lengthened and he definitely appeared larger. His neck had stiffened, while his whole body seemed to rise.

The younger bulls took a few steps back, fearing this monster bull striding away ahead of them.

The proud bull walked at a pace, due south for the duration of the day.

The trail of odoriferous urine marked his passage as it splashed against his back legs and seeped down onto his footpads. His metre-long penis was green and musthy.

By evening, sticky musth-specific temporis was visibly trickling down his cheeks from the swollen glands between his eyes and ear opening. Finally coming to a halt, he browsed and drank along the river bank, waiting for nightfall. He instinctively knew that conditions after dark would improve his communication skills. As the earth bowed farewell to the sun, Mafunyane moved to higher ground and browsed on the fruit of dense groves of wild date palms. Agitated, he paced to and fro, dribbling, weeping and very smelly. It was a dark night with no moon, and by now he'd had his fill of the large, drooping bunches of yellow fruit. He chewed on a frond.

Mafunyane suddenly stood quite still and listened. Then, in recognition of something he thought he heard, he again lifted his head and produced a musth rumble. He was flemering in true elephant style. He wrinkled up his trunk, blinked his eyes, announcing his condition and his wishes in low, attenuated, guttural murmurs. Once again he stood quite still, ears splayed, listening intently for a response.

Off in the distance, having dried out from their evening bath, a breeding herd of elephants was

settling down for the night. The Matriarch was in oestrus
and ready to mate: she would eventually become Mabitsi and
Limpopo's grandmother, but that was still far in the future.
She had called the herd to a high point on the river bank,
which had been excavated by previous floodwaters. The roots
of many ana trees, just producing their new flush, dangled
over the high banks. Their pale green leaves contrasted with
the darker, seasoned riverine forest.

A flock of some thirty Crested Guineafowl sauntered onto the
scene. Their heads were adorned with
curly, black crowns of fine short
feathers. The busy birds had
sinister expressions on their
faces and called in repetitive
bursts, exclaiming *Such
good luuuuck! Such good
luuuuck!* As the Matriarch
reached up to strip off some of
the succulent new leaves from
the ana tree, she checked
her reach and froze like a
sculpture of some ancient
royal elephant queen.

From the north, there was the
unmistakable low tremble of a musth rumble. The
deep tone resembled that of a famous bull she had previously
encountered. His tusks were the longest she had every seen,
and she very distinctly remembered how rough he had been.

The cow's response was immediate as she produced an
oestrus rumble. The quiet night air gave clarity to this
nocturnal conversation, and repeated rumbles back and forth
worked the two respondents into a frenzy.

By morning Mafunyane had moved closer to the breeding herd, and once the Matriarch encountered the mix of musth odours, emanating off the bull's body, she began to urinate and announced her intentions to the universe with a roar of excitement.

Mafunyane entered the fray only to be confronted by two other suitors. We'll see, he thought as he strode out to meet his adversaries, while producing a dexterous trunk and foot dance. With his head and tusks held high, Mafunyane marched headlong into battle.

He swaggered towards the two younger bulls. They shook their heads at the oncoming giant. As Mafunyane approached the younger bulls with their ears flapping, they swirled and fled.

The younger bulls stood some way off. Mafunyane approached once again, looming above the less experienced animals, and with a swift shake of his head he beat his ears against the side of his neck. The sound was like the crack of a whip against a tree stump. He then angled his huge body and approached the younger bulls, crab-like, in the most intimidating fashion. It was enough. The younger bulls turned tail and ran.

Mafunyane turned his attention to the Matriarch. She had left some damp evidence of her condition in the forest. The bull touched the urine patch with the tip of his extended trunk, leaving it in position for only a moment.

He then lifted his trunk and inserted it into and onto the upper level of his open mouth. On his palate was his Jacobson's organ, the gland that would, in the flash of an elephant's eye, confirm his suspicions.

Yes, this cow was his.

She too meant business and would be receptive to his amorous advances.

Mafunyane took up his guard while showing compliance as he shuffled the Matriarch away from the herd. She obeyed. By this stage her own temporal glands had erupted, and a gooey liquid caused her wrinkled cheeks to appear damp.

Within the secrecy of the outer shaded areas of the ana trees, the elephants mated. The great bull looked magnificent as he rose high onto the rear of the smaller cow. He penetrated her, releasing the semen which carried the genes of his bloodline. His huge tusks steadied the Matriarch as he placed them on each side of her wide grey body. There they stood for a moment frozen in time, motionless for this historic encounter. Then both animals produced a pandemonium rumble.

Eventually Mafunyane reversed and the Matriarch moved forward. She stood for a moment and then rejoiced. She produced a series of loud base-to-tenor boomed notes, repeated many times. The sounds reached a crescendo of choruses and then reduced and dwindled completely.

The Matriarch moved away a short distance from the scene and began to trumpet in disorganised blasts, accompanied by other wheezy, excited sounds.

Other members of the herd trundled onto the scene and trumpeted in a chorus of joyous approval. With ears flapping, the adult females urinated together and smelt the spot where the union had occurred. Oestrus calls resumed, followed by pockets of rumbles – and then there was silence.

The other cows in the herd stood quite close to the Matriarch throughout the night. They jostled for a position to be close to their leader, seeming to wish her well with comforting infrasound songs of congratulations.

By dawn of the following day Mafunyane had moved away, perhaps in search of other duties. Three moons after the event, Mafunyane, accompanied by his askaris, returned to the privacy of the Shingwedzi River to lead his quiet and introverted existence.

Twenty-two moons after the event, the Matriarch gave birth to the calf who would one day become Mabitsi's mother. She was perfect and resembled her father. The calf grew in stature and fortitude.

One midwinter's day she was browsing on the extended whip-like fronds of a shaving brush combretum growing along the banks of a sandy rivulet. An adult cow standing next to her was pushing her head against the white stem of a partially debarked knobthorn tree. The tree trunk snapped, causing two of the sub-adult bulls to jostle the young cow to one side. She lost her footing and fell across the splintered, one metre high upright stem of the tree. One spike of the jagged, brown core of the trees heartwood pierced her ear halfway from its outer margin, tearing it open. A flap as long as her young tusks fell, leaving her ear torn and tattered. It would remain a recognisable deformity throughout her life.

3

Lord Rijhna

4 years or 48 moons after the birth of Mabitsi

Elephants have been put to work in South East Asia for millennia. Powerful relationships between people and elephants have been embroidered into the very fabric of historical mythology.

The elephant has been revered, worshipped and exalted in India, Burma, Thailand, Vietnam, Cambodia and Sri Lanka for thousands of years. Lord Rijhna, at a time lost in history, was appointed as custodian of all the elephants in the world.

In modern times the role of the elephant has changed, and public consciousness has drawn people who care about elephants together, in protest against the traditional methods of subduing wild captive animals.

A mythological synthesis between men and elephants has evolved into a story to assist people to acknowledge their respective roles.

Lord Rijhna, it is said, has the head of an Asian elephant, two human arms and hands, a fat belly denoting his prosperity, and

a pair of grey legs and elephant footpads. His soft, cushioned feet allow Rijhna to tread gently through the wilderness, between and amongst people, and the passage of time.

Rijhna's elephant and human form enables him to speak for and on behalf of both the elephants and the people.

Folklore informs us that on a day preceding the onset of the monsoon rains in the fifth moon, clouds were banked against the mountain range of the Himalayas. As the clouds rose to meet the heavens, in a column twice as high as Mount Everest, they took on the shape and form of a bull elephant's head. From the head grew extended fan-shaped clouds with grey and pink linings. The last rays of the day cast by the sun god seemed to approve the process. People in the valleys gazed upwards in amazement as the elephant's head grew ears, which appeared to listen to the heavenly performance.

It was at this point that the people exclaimed, 'It's a wonderment. It's Rijhna!'

As the ears rose above the head, the great cumulus elephant trumpeted a series of base-toned warning rumbles. He blinked his eyes and streaks of light flashed around his temple. His trunk emerged. It grew and moved downwards, blowing torrents of warming air towards the earth, bending the trees and the grass and whipping up a dust storm that caused the watchers to scurry for shelter.

It is recorded in the ancient myths of the mountains that Lord Rijhna swayed his head and, following a few more rumbles to confirm his intentions, there were echoes in the canyons that caused the ground to shudder as he stamped his authority on the region.

The elephant god of the sky blinked and from his temporal glands, at a point between the bright lights and the front of his head, moisture was exuded and ran down the sides of his face. The fluid was blown about by this tumult, spreading it in all directions.

The drops plummeted earthwards, raining upon the mountains and swelling the streams which cascaded towards the valleys, and beyond. The people clapped and rejoiced at the relief that Rijhna had brought upon the landscape, immediately appointing him as the elephant god, the god of prosperity and the god of moisture and relief.

Lord Rijhna had, as his companion, a beautiful young girl who rode in a cart drawn by two wild, black mountain sheep. As the dark clouds collided with the valleys below, the girl and the sheep emerged from the navel of his fat extended belly. The high-sided cart rolled down Lord Rijhna's legs and onto the hillside. Its heavy spoked wheels creaked as it lumbered awkwardly over the rough terrain and into the valley. The sheep displayed their curving horns with a large black boss protruding from the centre of their shaggy heads. Their armour looked formidable as they bleated out a blessing to all who stood and watched. The girl had dark flowing hair

and her face showed only love and tranquillity. Her eyes were as grey as tropical pearls and shone a welcome.

Gifts of flowers and berries collected from the mountains were piled high on the cart behind where the girl sat. She held in her hand a plaited whisk made from the tail hairs of an elephant and a water buffalo. As she passed through the villages she handed out the produce from her cart, offering the people gifts and wishing them prosperity and joy.

The ceremony lasted for one short hour and they were then gathered up by the night and hidden in a dark, secret envelope of wonderment and reflection. Amongst the people in all the villages, on the mountains and in the valleys, there was silence, and then the rain came; falling in sheets of relief.

Lord Rijhna's loud warning rumbles were intended to caution people to improve their relationships with elephants; not to subdue them with beatings, not to attempt to break their spirit by harsh treatment and the cruel use of the bull hook. Elephants have the ability, he advised, to understand a more gentle approach to their taming and training, and like the squirrel hunter of Africa, their only real ally was patience.

In 1989, the Queen Mother of King Rama IX of Thailand (guided, perhaps, by Lord Rijhna, together with the proposed ban on the illegal opium trade by the United Nations Organisation) declared the felling of the teak resources of that country against the law. Hundreds of elephants became unemployed overnight.

The Thai people set about the planting of millions of hectares of teak seedlings. Poppy fields were abandoned, to be replaced by gardens of garlic and litchi orchards, and opium pots were smashed. Power and phone lines were extended to the furthest reaches of the kingdom in the hillside villages – and a new era was established. Tourism was popularised to extol the gentle nature of the Thai people and their elephants.

Elephants were relieved from their labours in the forest and gathered into sanctuaries to interact with people and live a life of integration and harmony, in a cross-species association with people. They were taught to lift people onto their backs for tranquil rides through the tropical forests, understanding the bilateral ask-and-reward principle now instilled and practised between people and elephants in both Africa and Asia. In twelve hundred moons from now, the mature teak trees in Thailand will be felled, bringing wealth and prosperity to one of only a few countries that have planned its future. The process is being sustained by the forest.

Troubled and testing times for other parts of the world, though, lay ahead.

In 1994, when a moratorium was brought about on the culling of the elephants in South Africa's Kruger National Park, Lord Rijhna realised that he no longer retained his long-distance influence over Africa's elephants. It was at this time that Rijhna sought advice from the heartland of the continent, from the Africans themselves. This required the appointment of a replacement African elephant goddess.

So on an allotted day and on the recommendation of Lord Vishnu, Rijhna retreated into the mountains ahead of a train of a hundred cumulus elephants. He camped above the snow-covered treeline and there, while facing west, where he imagined he could see the shores of Africa, he opened his ears once again and produced a series of extended pleading rumbles. He stood quite still, listening; wishing for a response; but the airwaves were silent. There was no acknowledgement of his appeal.

He would have to try again, after nightfall.

4

The birth of a star, Mabitsi

The sky seemed to lie in wait for a signal. It was that time of the year. There was a dawn dampness in the air as the sun rose above the horizon, illuminating the landscape. The parched African earth showed the harshness of the dry months, but within the unfolding of this theatre of seasonal change, a quiet miracle of life was about to enrich the lives of a small herd of elephants. They had gathered above the sandy banks of the Ntsumaneni ravine which cut through the Lebombo Mountain range, just south of the Olifants River in the Kruger National Park.

A young cow with a torn left ear had mated with a bull with tattered ears. She was inexperienced in matters of birth, and had tried to slip away unnoticed so that she could drop her calf in a dense homogenous glade of Lebombo ironwood trees, high on the red cliffs which kept watch over a pool in the river. Near to where she stood, along the extended mountain range, were three larger trees of the same species. Evergreen, with their long slender straight trunks and moderately spread crowns,

they loomed over the smaller trees while offering shelter to the young cow. She was in her two-hundred-and-fortieth moon.

Repetitive floodwaters had seen the banks of the river sculptured into uneven landmarks, exposing centuries of sediment, each with its own history of the past.

The young cow, now into her fourth tooth and fearful of her own ignorance, had released tell-tale infrasound signals, picked up on the airwaves by the herd, as she crept quietly into the grove of trees. In collaboration with the Matriarch, she had chosen this particular area of The Park for very specific and far-sighted reasons. She needed to pass on strategic information to the newborn calf, for he would carry superior genes.

With care and respect, the Matriarch of the herd, the one with the tusk that curved outwards, followed the young cow. This cow was her younger sister. She retained an appropriate distance and an attentive ear.

The pregnant cow knelt and strained, her round body borrowing strength from one of the rough tree trunks in the forest. A flood of warm fluid burst from her rear, washing and cleansing her flanks while she held her breath. With another heave, a light dove-grey bulge appeared from a reclusive opening between her bulbous loins. The effort caused her tail to rise and at that moment there was a deluge of steaming liquid that accompanied the amniotic sac. It contained four slippery truncated legs, an elongated tubular nose and a rotund body. The large ears seemed glued to the side of his gentle head, and her calf plunged onto the dry river bank.

Cautiously, with her right front foot, the cow touched the motionless lump incarcerated in his birth sack. The baby kicked his tiny feet in response. She then knelt forward and inserted her tusk, freeing the calf from the membrane, and there Mabitsi the elephant lay, exposed on the high river bank, taking his first breath.

While the young mother stood submissively on the eastern side of the dense thicket of young ironwoods, three striped nyala ewes standing at the water's edge stared up at her with the expectant awe of a group of student midwives. Mabitsi lay quite still for a moment, exhausted by the effort of his birth, his wide eyes stark with the anticipation of life's mysteries. The calf struggled twice to raise his head and move his four awkward legs, but fell back, lying still while releasing a stream of scentless baby elephant breath. The nyalas moved up the bank from the river bed and sauntered away into the riverine undergrowth. They had done their job.

The young mother swung round, her trunk following the swathe of her body like a fire-hose searching to extinguish some invisible flame. The tip of her trunk came to a controlled halt as it cast around, enquiring with regard to this fragile motionless lump on the spiky forest floor. Her heart pounded and pride and adrenalin mixed in her veins. Instinct caused her to swirl again in a full circle, almost accounting for her loss of footing as she scanned the groves of dense raisin bushes and scattered buffalo thorns on the banks of the river.

As the cow moved, a single Swainson's Francolin, his wattled neck held high, exploded triumphantly into the air and came to roost in the low branches of the tree where the elephants stood. He puffed out his tunic and preened one of his impressive spurs as though to sharpen it, like a swordsman honing his blade in preparation for a duel. He held his head forward and, with a solemn series of tenor trills, announced to the world that a birth had occurred.

Led by the other cows, the small patiently waiting herd of fourteen lumbered onto the scene and busied themselves with inquisitiveness. Mabitsi lay wide-eyed as the Matriarch proudly prodded her grandson and accompanied the motion with a low soothing rumble.

There was dust in the air.

The tones were deep and calming, the resonance even and reassuring. They flowed through Mabitsi's skin and entered his body, where they were absorbed and stored in his tiny elephant soul.

With the sun now at its zenith, Mabitsi's ears snapped loose from his baby head and flapped rhythmically, pumping as they cooled his body.

To the young cow's surprise, there was another downpour of warm moist tissue, as the afterbirth fell from her body, where it had nurtured Mabitsi for the past twenty-two months. This sodden pink carpet fell on the struggling calf, as though to anoint him. The cow turned and picked up the bundle of wet tissue with her left tusk and tossed it away, over her head. It landed in the branches of one of the ironwoods some distance from where she stood.

Klaserie and Letaba, a couple of boisterous young bull calves born in two previous seasons, pushed through the throng of eager onlookers, their trunks moving forward as they pressed for view, eager to offer an opinion. Letaba bugled his approval and then fell over a discarded river stone washed aside by some previous flood. He righted himself and shook his head with embarrassment. Turning on his heel, he rushed away from the herd, bugling his complete approval at the skills of his aunt. Not quite looking at what he was doing, he plunged headlong into a knobthorn stump, winding himself. In his annoyance he stormed off again – this time without a sound – to stand quietly some distance from his fascinated family. His mother quickly recovered and disciplined him with a prod to the ribs. His cousin, Klaserie, remained aloof and superior. He looked once; shook his head and then stood on a caterpillar he had observed crossing his pathway, then sauntered off to stand alone. He longed for his own mother.

To the sounds of this juvenile confusion, Mabitsi lurched to his feet, teetering as he balanced with some degree of difficulty on his round footpads, his tiny trunk swaying clownishly off his damp head.

The young mother, followed by a number of her female companions and a series of social rumbles, scanned the evidence of her son's birth with curiosity. As Mabitsi searched for the first mouthful of protective colostrum from his mother's breast, he was forming a bond with someone that would become his very best friend for the next ninety moons.

Unknown to this suckling elephant and his mother, on the sixtieth moon anniversary of his own birth, called 1994 by humans in the West, the carefully orchestrated reduction of the elephant population in the Kruger National Park would cease. The annual elephant cull would be discontinued, and there would be a transfer of authority over the custodianship of Africa's elephants. Tranquillity would return to the herds.

Perhaps Lord Rijhna, the Asian god of elephants, was losing his influence, tiring of observing at long distance, growing old. Perhaps there was, after nearly two thousand-and-four-hundred moons, a need for a change in the custodianship of the African Elephants; a transfer of authority.

Perhaps the process required an African way with the acknowledgement of the principles of the spirit of *ubuntu*. Rijhna had reflected for some time on these matters and would seek the advice of wise African counsellors to help in the naming and appointment of his successor.

This new African elephant goddess would follow the ideals of *ubuntu*, which required a fresh understanding of a rich traditional African philosophy. In the roots of *ubuntu* lay morality, humaneness, compassion, caring, understanding and empathy. *I am because you are.* A new custodian of all the African elephants would be appointed at the appropriate time; her title had already been proposed. But this would only occur when the time was right – when Lord Rijhna would retreat into the mountains of the Himalayas.

In the meantime, Mabitsi's mother looked down at her calf with protective pride and wished she could inform him immediately of the significance of his birthplace; why this particular vantage point in the entire park was so important to elephants, and why so many elephant ghosts and ancient fear rumbles still echo in the gorge below where they stood. But this would have to wait until Mabitsi entered his sixtieth moon. Only then would they return for a comprehensive explanation.

Mabitsi gazed upwards towards his mother. The now cloudless sky filled his eyes with a look of compliance. The rest of the small herd gathered round and listened as the new-born calf produced just one soft treble rumble, securing a bond with his mother.

21·08·2006

5

Knobnose kills a boy

11 years or 132 moons after the birth of Mabitsi

The twin teenagers in the Tsonga village woke an hour before dawn. The early morning was silent, save for the lamenting call of the fiery-necked night jar and the chirp of a cricket in the thatch of the boys' hut. It was constructed in the typically African pole-and-dagga style, with dry red clay packed between and around a lattice work of saplings, measuring some four metres in diameter. The roofs of all four of the families' huts had been neatly thatched over a period of three seasons, as and when good quality thatching-grass became available.

This family homestead, which stood within the larger community hut-town, was the traditional rural-home retreat of the Malemela family. Bebedu and Grace had seven children. The Malemela family were members of the Mnisi community, which consisted of eleven villages and seven thousand people.

The community had established its traditional roots approximately twenty kilometres from the boundary of the

Kruger National Park, near the Orpen entrance gate in the centre of The Park. They existed primarily as subsistence farmers and migratory workers to the gold mines around Johannesburg.

The twin boys were twelve years old and were expected at the Hluvukani Primary School gates by seven-thirty sharp. They had three-and-a-half hours to complete their duties in the family's bean field before then. One of the boys also had an English essay to complete: time was of the essence.

The family dog stretched and yawned as the twins splashed cold water over their faces and heads and quickly devoured some firm, cold maize porridge, cooked the previous evening. Over their breakfast they sloshed a delicious relish of boiled beans, tomatoes and onions, spiced with a tin of pilchards in tomato sauce.

The front door of their hut hung on two hinges made from thick strips of truck-tyre rubber. The door scraped on the dry dung floor of the hut as it opened, causing a group of sleepy chickens to flutter down from their perch and immediately start scratching in the soil outside the hut as the light from the hurricane lantern shone out into the cool dawn air.

The boys trod with caution, wary of opportunistic scorpions in search of cockroaches that might flee the open hut. They each grabbed a hoe and climbed onto the bicycle they shared; one of them on the cross bar, balancing the hoe between the handle-bars and his knees while facing sideways. The front tyre was slightly soft but there was no time to search for the pump. The boys set off for the field planted on rich alluvial soil which their father had established under the shade of a large sycamore fig tree, on the banks of a stream eleven minutes ride from their home. They whistled a duet to the national anthem, Nkosi Sikeleli Africa. They wondered why the tune so resembled a nursery rhyme their Sunday school teacher had taught them, called Incy-Wincy-Spider. The very last thing on their minds was the remainder of the homework the one boy still needed to complete.

As the boys approached the bean field, the first birds began their dawn chorus. While perched on the top of a lone paw-paw tree, a solitary black-eyed bulbul flaunted the yellow vent under his tail and sang loudly, *Just look at all that fruit; just look at all that fruit.* A lone crested francolin called a mournful plea for the warmth and security of the anticipated sun, and a herd boy cracked his long, plaited leather whip and drove the neighbour's twenty-three Nguni cattle into the river bed to drink from the sand weir that had been created there to divert the meagre stream into the bean field. The air was dry, crisp and filled with expectation, and the cloudless horizon had turned pink, putting the grey of the night to sleep. They stopped the bike and soaked up the moment. The first-born twin quickly recorded the brief event. He would translate this special scene onto his canvas during his art class later in the day. He loved art, and dreamed of becoming a sculptor and exhibiting his work in Cape Town one day. He wished to help other people capture the glow of the Lowveld.

They pushed the bike across the headland of the field and parked it against the fig tree. The hoes were put to work immediately. The plants were in their third week of flowering, and the green beans from the first week's pollination were now nearly ready to pick. The beans were succulent and sweet. While guiltily looking up, the boys each plucked off a few beans and quickly chewed them, relishing the fresh taste. The two boys, working side by side, had another hour to finish weeding the last corner of the field. They would then open a small earth gate, allowing the water to flow into the furrows to irrigate the first few lines of the bean crop. Bebedu would arrive and take over their watering duties when the boys left. As they worked they hummed tunes they knew from the radio, concentrating on American rap. They didn't quite know what it all meant, but they were committed to supporting their brothers over the Atlantic: the two lads were lost in their dream-world of modernity.

They were watched by Knobnose the elephant, so named from the large growth positioned halfway down his trunk. He had pushed a section of the Kruger National Park's boundary fence down, while being pursued by a larger, more aggressive bull and had spent four days crop-raiding and being chased by villagers. Knobnose's entire body was flowing with testosterone. The young bull-elephant was experiencing his first musth and was irritated, confused and aggressive.

The smell of fresh beans growing on the Malemelas' field had drifted up the river bank as the first of the sun's rays had caused the air to swirl and rise, and now the lone elephant-bull stood quite still on the banks of the stream above the field. He was shielded by the fig tree and watched the two boys at work with their backs to him.

Slowly and silently, he slipped down the river bank, causing the dry leaves to rustle under his footpads as a few alluvial clay balls rolled into the sandy stream. One splashed into the weir. Utterly absorbed with their musical heroes, the boys never looked up. It was only when Knobnose, having filled his trunk with water, lifted his head to pour the liquid into his gaping pink mouth and down his throat that the gurgling, flushing sound caught the boys' attention. There, standing not fifteen paces from where they worked, stood the biggest elephant they had ever seen. Their bike was between them and the great beast, and their alternative route was over rough terrain through the bean field.

Simultaneously they hurled their hoes at the elephant while shouting for their mother, 'Mane! Mane! – and then they turned and fled in opposite directions.

One implement flew through the air, colliding with the side of the elephant's head and bouncing off his temporal area. Seeing the missile coming, Knobnose head-butted the handle of the hoe and, in instant annoyance, took off at high speed through the field after the younger twin. Within seconds the elephant was towering over the petrified boy. With his powerful trunk he lifted the screaming twin up and then thrashed his frail body to the ground, beating it numerous times onto a protruding granite boulder.

After what seemed like an age, he dropped the lifeless boy's body to the ground and then knelt forward, driving one of his tusks through the boy just above the navel. He then pressed his head against the dead boy, like a man squashing an ant under the sole of his shoe. The elephant stood up, trumpeted and then fled back and up the bank of the stream, where he disappeared into the mopani scrub.

The remaining twin had reached the path. Without looking back, he hurtled headlong towards the safety of his village. As he ran he stumbled and fell. He took shortcuts across loops in the path, tearing his legs and clothes against the sickle-bush thorn trees as they slowed his flight. He plunged headlong into a donga. He twisted his ankle in an ant-bear hole. Finally he arrived – exhausted, wide-eyed and breathless at his parents' hut, still shouting for his mother. Once inside, he gulped down a calabash of water and then spouted his story.

Bebedu summoned a large group of men from the village, one of whom had an old twelve-gauge shotgun and some number six bird shot, and off they marched to hunt the elephant. Half an hour later the angry hunters arrived at the sad scene, where they were met by a group of very agitated herd-boys and a few women who had been on their way to collect water. The elephant was reported to have departed the area and two of the men, skilled in the art of tracking, were put onto the spoor. They soon returned, explaining that the animal had headed straight back towards The Park.

The dead twin was gathered up and placed on a home-made stretcher of soft, leafy, branches, cut from the straight stems of young mopani trees and bound together with bark stripped from two or three raisin bushes. A few bean plants were removed from the field to cushion the stretcher, and the boy's scarred body was gently laid on it. His mother washed her son's cold skin in the weir, and covered the boy with a colourful batik-printed shroud she had brought with her. The family started their mournful trek back along the path.

As they swayed and ululated with grief on this midmorning winter's day, thoughts were stirring in the mind of the grieved father. Why was his son dead? Elephants had been part of their lives for generations. He and his father before him had always had to deal with crop-raiding elephants, yet seldom had this resulted in the death of either an elephant or a member of the communities bordering The Park. But in more recent times there had been a rise in the conflict-level between elephants and the local people. Why was it that the youngsters of today no longer understood how to behave in the presence of elephants when they were confronted by them in the bush or in the fields? What had caused the loss of these traditional links with the wilderness? And why was it that recently there were more elephant visits to their fields? Children nowadays knew nothing. His sons had no interest in the wild or its trees and plants, used so successfully by himself and his father before him. He questioned why it was that his sons and daughters wore such ill-fitting clothes and kept their hair combed out and shiny. They listened to the most obscure music that seemed to thump without any melody: the only traditional instrument left in these modern bands was the drum.

It saddened the old man to hear how his sons had simply run away from the elephant, instead of turning and talking to it, confronting it, persuading it to leave in peace by simply shooing it away. Perhaps they should introduce a type of wilderness school to re-acquaint children with some of these ancient links with wild places, animals and plants, these important components, these lost African life-skills.

He had been told by one of the village elders at their monthly meetings that people from faraway countries were keen to visit the Kruger National Park to see the animals and to experience the wide-open spaces. That's why so much effort had been placed on stopping the poaching in The Park. But the elephants seemed to be a problem. There seemed to be more and more of them and they tore down the trees and invaded the farmers' crops more regularly. The old man made a point of remembering to speak to the gozie (the chief) on this subject when they next met.

The old man also needed to speak to his son. 'My boy, do you not remember the story of the young boy of your age, a boy-hunter from the !Kung people in the Kalahari Desert in the north? He was once confronted by an elephant while tracking an eland bull he had shot with a poisoned arrow. On seeing the great beast towering above him he fell to the ground, becoming an *ulumbyne* – a monitor lizard – and slithering away, avoiding a confrontation with an animal two hundred times his size. The elephant apparently trumpeted once and then turned and left.'

'Oh,' said the boy, 'I had forgotten, Daddy. We were afraid of the elephant. We just turned and ran away; and now my brother is dead! I'm so, so sorry,' the boy sobbed.

His brother's coffin was delivered the following day. He was laid to rest in a shallow grave two days later, next to where Bebedu had buried his father, his mother and another of his children, a nine-year-old daughter. The older women in the community poured out their grief by ululating for most of the afternoon and evening. The boy's siblings had been summoned from the city where they were studying, and for a week the family spewed out their devastation at the loss of a son and brother.

On the morning of the seventh day following the tragedy, the students boarded the bus and returned to their studies, and Bebedu and Grace continued with their duties in the bean field. They needed to pay close attention now, as they had to harvest a bumper crop to pay for the additional expenses surrounding the death of their son.

In December of the same year when the exam results arrived for the remaining twin, his father was pleased and asked him, '*Loko u heta xikolo u ta endla yini, Thomas*'? What do you intend doing with your life now, Thomas?

'Vito ra mina a ka hari Thomas, Papa, Vito ra mina I Hosi Ndlopfu Yi Kulu'.

My name is no longer Thomas, Daddy. It is Master of the Large Elephants.

He went on. *'Ni ta ya dyundza swa ku hlayisa tumbuluko. Ni lava ku tiva hikokwalaho ke yini ndlopfu yak u vana kunubu a mivini yi dlaye buti wa mina na swona ni lava ku pfuna ku sivela kuri swi nga humelei vanwana. Hikwalaho ka yini a nga yimanga thlelo rin'wana ra ndzelekano? Hi lava ku tshama hi ku rula na tindlopfu, Papa. Vanhu vo tala vari kuna tindlopfu to tala e Kruger Tanga wa Swiharhi lero ku hava na ndhawu ya tona hinkwato.'* I'm going to study nature conservation. I need to know why the elephant with a knob on his trunk killed my brother. I want to help prevent the same from happening to others. Why did he not stay on the other side of the fence? We need to live in peace with the elephants, Daddy. Many people say there are just too many elephants and not enough space for them all.

The old man turned and walked away. He lit his pipe and as he sat on a dry marula stump in front of his fire, the last rays of the setting sun receded over the mountains.

As the grey-haired man turned to pat his skinny dog, he noticed his remaining twin boy rolling tufts of fibrous tissue he had extracted from the waxy, spiny-tipped leaf of a sisal plant. By rolling the fibres on his knee with the flat of his hand and by adding new pieces as he worked, he was creating a tough, natural twine. As the string grew in length, he rolled it into a ball.

Their eyes met. I Hosi Ndlopfu Yi Kulu said, *'Papa, hi lava ku fulela na kambe yindlu liya. Timbalelo ti ta tiyisa na ku sirelela ku fulela ngopfu. I siku ra wean ra ku velekiwa mundzuku, leyi I nyiko ya mina ka wena.'* Daddy, we need to re-thatch this house of yours this year. This natural string will bind the thatch more securely. It's our birthday tomorrow. This is my gift to my dead brother.

A tear rolled down the old man's cheek as he saw his wife Grace standing in the doorway of their hut. Her hands were clasped together and her gap-toothed smile seemed to give him the strength he so desperately needed. He turned to warm his hands at the fire, and the dog barked once as the last bare-necked chicken flew up to roost away from the genet it sensed prowling in the shadows beyond the flickering flames.

6

The birth of a patriarch

6 years or 72 moons prior to the birth of Mabitsi

It was August, seventy-two moons prior to the birth of Mabitsi. Warm winds created dust storms over the Lowveld, blinding the landscape for hours every day. The dry season was coming to an end, and the southern area of the Kruger National Park was dry, parched, and brittle.

A male Bateleur Eagle flew, tumbled and soared on the wind turbulence for the sheer thrill of flight. His short tail and specific style of arched angular turns distinguished him from all other raptors when he was airborne. His white under-wings with single, broad, black bands at the tips of each wing feather, together with his red legs and face mask, helped to confirm him as master aviator over Africa's plains.

An elephant cow in her four-hundred-and-fiftieth moon stood ready to deliver her sixth calf. She was a daughter of Mafunyane, the magnificent bull from the north. The cow, who had mated with a wandering bull from the south, was proud and confident of the task to be performed. Together with four other older cows and in the company of the Matriarch, who had lost the end of her tail after being attacked by crocodiles when she was much younger, the elephants had gathered together under a large weeping boerbean tree. The boerbean trees were some of only a few species that retained their leaves that far into the winter. Dark-red flowers had emerged from the tips of the branches and rained drops of nectar onto the forest floor. The trees are often referred to as the rain tree, as their blossom emergence often coincided with the onset of the wet months. The dense, green, foliage offered cool respite to the elephants from the wind and the dry spring heat.

The supportive cows in the herd produced comforting rumbles and the front of the Matriarch's head reverberated with tones of encouragement and approval.

As the moist package containing the newborn male calf slid from a recess between the elephant cow's hind legs, she turned to examine her infant. She inserted her tusk through the membrane of the amniotic sac and gently tore it open. The mother then peeled away the bag, exposing the head of a tiny, damp, hairy, light-grey elephant calf and, with a prod, Tembo drew his first breath of African spring air.

The breath was a gulp which seemed to startle him and as his floppy little trunk moved from its birth position, there was a faint bugle of gratitude. The air was dusty and Tembo coughed and blinked his small, dark eyes. The Matriarch moved forward to complete her inspection, the stump of her tail wagging with approval. She leaned down and carefully removed cobwebs of birth tissue still attached to the calf's face and eyes. She then lifted her head and produced a low, protracted rumble of complete acclaim and joy. The calf was perfectly healthy and the image of his grandfather. What did everyone expect?

All the cows shuffled closer. With other members of the herd in attendance, Tembo's mother picked up the wet birth sac, walked a short distance from where they were gathered and dropped it behind a pile of boulders scattered randomly on the edge of the clearing. The balance of the calves had moved in to voice their opinion. Each of the elephants demanded a view. Emotions were running high and the atmosphere was filled with elephant discussion rumbles. This was a very important occasion.

Tembo lay quite still, not sure what to make of all the fuss. The sun had travelled past its zenith and, assisted by the wind, the calf's skin quickly dried. His little ears flapped loose from his head and Tembo rolled over onto his knees, teetered once, and then stood tottering on his four soft footpads.

He was up! He shook his awkward baby elephant head and waggled his trunk and then took four wobbly steps towards his mother to nurse.

The excitement which galvanised the adults had grown to an explosive level and, conducted by the Matriarch, the entire herd burst into a series of trumpets and bugles. The chorus of an elephant choir and orchestra boomed into the dry spring atmosphere. Junior and senior members sounded off in a glorious celebration of Tembo's birth. The new calf suckled at his mother's breast as the voices of his happy family filled every bone of his tiny body with joy and confidence.

The merry-making continued for the rest of the day, with all the members of family returning at regular intervals to again examine and bond with the newborn calf. Tembo stayed very close to his mother, shy and overwhelmed. As evening approached the herd moved to a muddy recess they knew still contained some run-off from the previous rainy season. Here they mud-bathed in further boisterous festivity to honour the newest member of the family. Tembo wasn't yet ready for his first swim, as his umbilical cord attachment was still damp and vulnerable to infection. His mother dutifully held him close underneath her belly as she slurped her fill of the muddy water.

That night the elephants moved away from the scene of Tembo's birth, away from the prying eyes of the jackals and hyenas who they knew would discover the amniotic sac and tissue which had nurtured the calf for twenty-two months. Tembo lay between his mother's front feet, with his diminutive trunk curled up securely next to his baby elephant head. There he slept like the cherub he was.

But Tembo was an August calf, gregarious, resolute, experimental and ready to establish himself in elephant society. As the weeks unfolded and the earth saluted and greeted many moons, Tembo grew, guided and taught by his mother. From the outset, Tembo was an exploratory student and liked to play hide and seek. When in his thirtieth moon, he would sneak away to be alone and then attempt to produce a suckle rumble. He hadn't, of course, by this time suckled for many moons, so it didn't always come out quite as he had intended. To begin with, some of the females responded, but the adults quickly grew wise to Tembo's little game.

But Tembo's tendency to be alone – and to think for himself – would stand him in good stead.

7

A narrow escape for Tembo

4 years or 48 moons prior to the birth of Mabitsi

In the early nineties, Lord Rijhna was under pressure. International public opinion was weighing heavily on Park authorities to discontinue the annual culling of elephants in The Kruger National Park. The elephant god rose up and looked towards Africa for guidance.

But there was none. Dark clouds moved over The Park and there was consternation in the air.

Tembo's family had established itself in an area of The Park adjacent to Balule Game Reserve and Tembo was celebrating his thirty-first moon. He had wandered off some distance from the herd, re-assured by contented infrasound rumbles from his family. He was particularly interested in an undiscovered raisin bush. The fruit was ripe and a reddish-yellow to green in colour and had a sweet taste. As Tembo manoeuvred

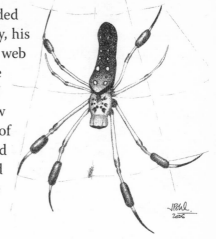

his way down an eroded embankment to a small valley, his face became entangled in the web of a Golden-orb Spider. As he cleared the sticky strands of silk from his eyelids, the yellow spider climbed onto the end of his trunk. The spider's legs had black and yellow segments and were long and gangling, while the abdomen was yellow and engorged. As the young elephant flicked the spider from the end of his trunk it flew high into a nearby tree, leaving a single cord of multiple-spun silk strands trailing from the spinnerets at the rear of the abdomen. The strands shone in the sunlight, but Tembo chose to ignore the whole affair, searching instead for the sweet raisins. He moved further down the embankment, carefully choosing his footing. As he reached the raisin bush, he heard an attenuated, droning noise approaching from the south east. The sound arrived on the prevailing wind, a sinister whir in its purposeful approach.

There was a concern rumble from Tembo's mother and as the helicopter appeared out of the bright morning sky, the Matriarch produced a fearful trumpet, the likes of which Tembo had never heard. The helicopter established itself overhead the group. A man holding a rifle to his shoulder leaned out of the side of the noisy aircraft.

Small projectiles were systematically released and flew towards each of the elephants. The small Scoline-laden syringes each found their mark, one after the other. Each elephant was darted while they huddled together, some distance from where Tembo stood alone in his private gully.

The Matriarch was the first to
teeter and collapse. The balance of the
herd clustered around her, producing just
about every elephant rumble and distress
call imaginable. The calves screamed above
the tone and purr of the chopper. The adult
cows roared, with the white rings around their
wide eyes shining like alabaster. Contact calls
rang out, between the now partially drugged
mothers and some of the calves. The calves
bellowed and groaned, until the final drug-laden
needle had delivered its tranquilliser and the last
elephant crumpled where it stood. Still conscious, though
immobilised, the group lay together, quite aware of the
battle being raged around them.

Tembo was just out of reach of the wind effect of the
helicopter, trapped in the small gorge. He tried without
effect to rise and join his family. He needed the comforting
reassurance of his mother.

The power blades of the chopper had whipped up the soil,
creating a dust bowl which further confused and frightened the
elephants, while simultaneously camouflaging the trapped calf.

While trying to exit the steep walls of the gully, Tembo
fell backwards in his confusion, and when he looked again,
he saw his mother's legs crease under her weight as she fell,
as though she was shocked and dying. Tembo's wise young
mind re-assessed his predicament and he checked himself for
a moment. Then he turned and fled.

As he climbed the opposite bank of the gully where he'd
been feeding, the helicopter landed and the men's focus
turned to the mass of eighteen elephants splayed on the floor
of the African plains. One man climbed onto the exposed side
of each animal and systematically brain-shot every candidate

with an FN military calibre assault rifle .762. The bullets were sharp-pointed, full-metal-jacket, copper-covered 270 grain standard issue. The dust swirled. It was early morning on a hot spring day and death hung in the air.

As the helicopter blades slowly came to rest, the members of the culling team stood watching the dead animals with compassion. These were tough days for conservationists, who spent most of their energy protecting and saving lives, and emotions ran high during the months when culling occurred in The Park.

The rifleman sat in the shade of a sausage tree close to where the carnage had taken place. He lay on his back with his hands folded behind his head. He had consciously moved away, to be alone and to reflect on the part he had to play in this elephant-culling programme. It saddened him as he reflected on the swiftness with which the whole affair had occurred. To minimise the animals' suffering was always his main objective.

Tembo made it to higher ground and lumbered off in the opposite direction, away from this fearful place. He ran in confused silence, understanding the dire need for self preservation. He tripped and staggered as he fled for his life, his legs appearing stiff as he bumbled away in fear and panic.

His trunk swung awkwardly as he moved, while away in the distance a Green-spotted Wood-dove called a mournful descending, *Your father's dead, your mother's dead, everybody's dead, boo, hoo hoo hoo hoo.* Tembo had lost all sense of direction. He stumbled over fallen logs and crashed through dense groves of mopani scrub. He meandered aimlessly up dry river beds and through herds of wildebeest, trumpeting and scattering them as he moved. Dancing herds of impala skipped and leaped, as though choreographed by Lord Rijhna himself. He spent one whole day standing hopefully next to a baobab tree, its grey, lumpy stem seeming to give him comfort.

As Tembo hobbled headlong, a snowstorm of white egrets rose from the mass of the black hides of a battalion of Cape Buffalo. They stood with their necks and heads held high, inquisitively observing the antics of this lone young elephant. Their snorts and mock-charges were of no concern to Tembo.

A flock of grey, speckled Helmeted Guineafowl, with their blue necks pulsating, torpedoed into the air as Tembo disturbed their feeding area in the long grass near a vlei. They all chattered with the stress of instant flight while announcing, *Good grrreeef, good grrreeef. Rrrreally!* A lone steenbok stood and stared as Tembo made his aimless getaway.

Evening approached. The night was dark and misty. Tembo could hear the droning call of hyenas, following his passage westward through the wilderness. Instinct forced him to keep moving, though he was debilitated, confused and consumed by loss and despair. He ambled on, his temporal lobes oozing a sticky liquid of fear and desperation.

Suddenly, Tembo was wide awake, the whites of his eyes showing, his tail standing straight up behind him. He had walked into the electrified game fence which demarcated the western boundary of The Park. Eight thousand volts of electricity had surged through his body. He swung round, trying to establish what it was that had so instantly invigorated his sense of awareness. How could such a state of exhaustion be so quickly and instantly remedied?

Five strands of wire entangled themselves around his head and front legs. His own strength surprised him as he tore the wires from his body and surged forward to escape the pulsating shocks. In an instant he was through the fence, heading on towards sounds and voices he could hear off in the distance.

He passed a drinking trough, where he briefly slaked his thirst, swallowing one trunkfull of water after the next. The whooping sounds of the hyenas were left well behind him. In his delirium and totally fatigued state, he eventually came to a standstill and fell abruptly asleep while leaning against the trunk of a dead knobthorn tree.

Tembo woke to the sound of human voices. As he turned his head, he caught the whiff of some rather pleasant-smelling food; a smell that was new to him. Tembo was confused and hungry. Inexplicably, one of the people moved towards him, offering him the contents of a silver bucket. The receptacle contained delicious compressed cubes. Tembo gulped them down and walked after the man as though he was a new friend. Tembo had arrived on Tshukudu Game Ranch and was under the care of the Sussens family, where he would spend the next sixteen years, or one hundred-and-ninety-two moons.

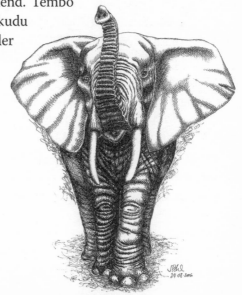

8

Instructions for dry times ahead

3 years or 36 moons after the birth of Mabitsi

The dry winter months in the Lowveld had moved beyond the end of the year and well into the forthcoming rainy season. The Matriarch with one tusk curved outwards had a deep sense of foreboding. She had once received a cryptic message, passed onto her by her mother, that had been sent in turn from her mother before her. The communication contained signs and insights of an impending drought. The Matriarch instinctively knew that difficult times were ahead. The absence of these tell-tale signs of rain troubled her. She stood alone on a section of open plain, with the herd browsing some distance away. She needed time to reflect and to explore the innermost sanctity of her memory. She needed to draw on her elephant bloodline. When was it that she'd last had this deep knowing; this quiet acceptance that their lives were about to change? She knew she carried great elephant responsibility. Her mother had empowered her with volumes of information, the importance of which was not always clear.

While standing alone and searching her mind for clues, the Matriarch raised her footpad above the earth. Vibrations and resonances could be picked up on the airwaves, assisting her. Ancient, stored energy fields were accessed through her feet as she concentrated. The herd moved on and the Matriarch rumbled to herself, willing the knowledge to surface. She spent the rest of the moon milling over these strange warning signs. In time, the answers would be forthcoming.

One evening after the earth had saluted the sun, there was a low rumble in the distance and a flash of coloured lights in the night sky. These colours were not the usual streaks and flashes associated with rain. These night-lights were far away, like distant fires on the horizon. But there was no smoke or smell of burning. On the third evening of these far-off coloured skies, it came to her. Dry times were ahead, and a huge sense of relief embraced the Matriarch. She now knew what her duties were, and as more elephant thoughts filtered through her mind she recalled the details of the Hill of Hope to the north.

Many gruelling days of marching had once taken her to the Hill of Hope, under her mother's guidance. The journey had begun from a point on the river where a large baobab grew. As she remembered the journey, she realised that her contented and relaxed life-style was about to change. A cold fear swept through her body and at that moment, she really missed her mother. Shades of doubt engulfed her and she swirled around looking for assistance, perhaps hoping to find her wise mother standing out on the fringe of the forest. But there were no elephants other than those of her family. She needed to guide her small herd north towards the high, steep, rocky Hill of Hope, which she had only ever seen once when she was very young. With her intelligent trunk and a discussion rumble, the Matriarch summoned Mabitsi's mother, the cow with the torn left ear, to her side. Mabitsi himself was in his thirty-seventh moon, well into his second molar.

He stood beside his mother, listening to, and feeling, the infrasound conversation between the two adults. The insights were intense and far-reaching. Mabitsi's half-sister, who had severe scarring right on the tip of her trunk, an old wound from a puff adder bite that had become necrotic, also moved closer to the young cow, joining her cousins Letaba and Klaserie. The four calves absorbed and recorded each and every sound and vibration.

Mabitsi felt sheets of anxiety ripple through his small elephant body. Although he couldn't fully comprehend the adult discussion, he knew that the information being imparted to his mother was of great elephant importance.

The story was a map. A low frequency guided tour of instruction, of how to get there.

The four calves heard and recorded how there would be the crossing of a dry, stony river bed, at a point where an enormous prepossessing upside-down tree; a baobab, grew. The tree had germinated at a time so far back that no elephant knew when this was. This was referred to by any elephant, in any herd, anywhere, as In The Beginning. Mabitsi learned that the tree was so large that fifteen fully-grown elephant bulls once stood around it, head to head, touching its smooth grey stem, yet there was still room for one more calf. Sheets of the same tree's fibrous main stem had been torn off by his ancestors during a devastatingly dry period, the evidence of which still showed. This had occurred in the year after his mother was born. The calves learned how the trunk of the tree was hollow and that a leopard had once reared her two cubs, deep in the bowels of this mark on the river bank where the crossing would occur. Rumour had it that one of the spotted cubs had been strangled by a python, with the mother leopard in her desperation unable to defend her offspring.

The calves listened intensely as the two adults disclosed further issues regarding the tree. Fascinated, the calves absorbed how large, round-eyed night birds with powerful talons and curved, devilish beaks would nest high in the limbs of the tree, rearing their young on the very mice so feared by all the elephants in the world.

The four calves learned that the tree had partially grown around a large black rock at its base and that the rock seemed to resemble the rear end of an elephant bull. This, they all thought, was very strange indeed.

At that moment, there was a series of prolonged discussion rumbles from the adults. The details of the message were reaching a critical point and Mabitsi felt his mother's trunk gently stroking his round head as she cleared a coagulation of white foam from his right eye. She was reassuring him and instructing him to listen. She realised how he had drifted away on a cloud of his own thoughts.

Once past the baobab whose naked, outstretched branches could be seen from a half a day's distance, the elephants would gather and feed until the earth dipped to greet the new moon.

On the evening following the crescent moon the herd, guided by this sliver of light, would head straight for the silhouetted skyline below the moon's left pointer on the horizon. They would walk at night only, for three full days. There might be no place to drink along the way and the small herd would be exhausted on their arrival at the Hill of Hope. The calves recorded how, as the grass dried up and the intense heat transformed the days, water would become more difficult to find. They would see how the adults disgorge stored water from deep within their own stomachs to cool themselves and the calves in times of prolonged heat. They heard how the lights in the night sky would flash with strange colours, warning the elephants that no rains would come. It was recorded how these signs would cause the older family members to gather together and produce multiple resonances of intense fearful rumbles that would persist for days on end, frightening the youngsters. Clearly the adults were mulling over these very issues. Along this torturous journey there would be many other perils – deep canyons, steep hillsides and one notorious pride of specialist elephant-eating lions.

The calves pushed even closer at the mention of lions. Letaba and Klaserie moved around, trying to nuzzle between the adults for greater security.

Mabitsi fell asleep on his feet. He dreamed thoughts liberated from far down within his young elephant soul.

He and his friends were in a muddy pool, completely submerged, with only the tips of their gangly trunks showing above the water. Steamy breath burst from the surface as he submerged himself entirely, turning upside down and allowing the breeze to catch and cool all four of his round grey-brown footpads. He then rolled over and raised his head out of the water. Muddy slime dripped from his long protective eyelashes.

He woke with a jolt as the small herd, now fully briefed, quietly moved off into a dense grove of spiny, slender, Three-hooked Thorn Trees. Mabitsi browsed on their lower branches despite the extremely thorny shoots. The tree was in full bloom and its light, creamy-white, caterpillar-shaped flowers tickled the end of Mabitsi's trunk as he plucked the blooms from the prickly branches. His mother stripped off the tasty, yellow, flaky bark, offering slivers of it to him.

As the herd pushed on through the dry central to northern region of The Park, the Matriarch spent time communicating with other elephant herds in the area.

There were continuous low rumbles of recognition between the families. The Matriarch noticed numerous large groves of trees and Mabitsi and his older sister boggled at the abundance of small flocks of important-looking Ground Hornbills. The male birds, with their red eye wattles and throat pouches, seemed to have scant regard for the two boisterous young elephants.

Mabitsi noticed these turkey-sized birds delivering lizards and frogs to fairly large holes in tall trees quite high off the ground. He rather liked these black walking birds. They had beautiful blue eyes and long eyelashes. On one occasion he watched in amazement as two Ground Hornbills found a leopard tortoise. The birds proceeded to pierce a hole right

through its shell, pull out the legs and gobble up the entire insides of this harmless little mobile stone.

The herd, led by the Matriarch, moved north, heading for the baobab on the banks of the river. Mabitsi shuddered at the thought of the large tree but he waggled his trunk and shook his head, trying to build up his own confidence. The day drew to a close and the elephants stopped to drink from a pool in the river. A crocodile lay on the opposite bank of the river, and two terrapins sunned themselves on a fallen tree trunk. Great yellow fever trees lined the water, tall and offering ample shade and browsing for the elephant family as they rested overnight. The trees bore fruity pods and the young elephants stretched their little trunks high into the lower branches, plucking off bunches of the tender, chewy seed pods.

Soft vibrations entered the elephant calves' bodies and they understood how the resonance was a clear instruction that it was safe to bath prior to lying down for the night. They confidently understood that the adults would remain alert for the duration of the night.

Mabitsi's half-sister also dreamed, but her memories were less pleasant than Mabitsi's. Her feet and trunk twitched as she lay close to where her mother stood.

The herd had been browsing in the long grass on the open veld. The hot summer sun baked down on the red earth where they walked. The first rains had fallen and field mice and frogs moved freely through the lush surface vegetation on an open patch of sodic soils between the areas of red clay.

Her elephant family had all proceeded towards the salty pan when something caught the young female calf's notice, just to the right of her path. Instinctively, she moved away as a deep, steady, hissing alarmed her. As she moved, she stood on a branch close to where a puff adder lay. The snake was as thick as the end of the young elephant's trunk and superbly camouflaged against the mix of red, brown and grey soils.

The disturbance caused the snake to strike forward with lightning speed, attaching itself onto the lower finger of the elephant's trunk. She let out a squeal, the intensity of which had never before been heard by her mother or Mabitsi.

The young female calf reared backwards with the fat reptile still attached to her trunk and then lashed forward, attempting to dislodge it.

The serpent hit the ground with the force of a large coil of rope lashing a dockside, and was swept aside and plucked loose by the force.

It slithered away in an instant, hissing its disapproval. But it was too late. The cytotoxic venom had penetrated deeply into the soft sensitive tissue around the tip of the elephant's trunk and spread quickly through her bloodstream. The young animal squealed with fear and agony. She thrashed her trunk in all directions, believing that something was still attached to it.

Mabitsi rushed to his half-sister's assistance, offering soothing audible rumbles and bugling incessantly to frighten off whatever it was that had so disturbed his sister.

The calf's mother seemed to know instinctively what had occurred and took the young calf's trunk into her mouth, biting gently on its tip. The pain was unbearable and the calf tore her trunk from her mother's jaws. She fell over, rolling and squealing in agony.

The dam lifted her agonised calf with the assistance of her trunk and tusks.

The tip of the calf's trunk began to swell, close and throb. Tears streamed down the calf's cheeks and she whimpered pathetically.

The following morning the tip of her trunk was the size and colour of an overripe monkey-orange fruit and the tiny limb throbbed continuously. There was one very sad and self-absorbed little elephant in the herd. The mother suckled her daughter throughout the days that followed. The flesh temperature at the end of the small elephant's trunk rose to forty-one degrees as the necrosis set in. A large black scab formed around the tip of her trunk. After eight days it burst, revealing a greenish, reddish substance, and the putrid smell of decaying flesh.

Only then did the pain begin to subside.

Her mother, the Matriarch of the herd, spent much of her day searching for, and debarking, hairy caterpillar-pod shrubs and fed soft, light grey slivers of bark to her calf. Mabitsi stayed close to his half-sister, confused at her misery.

The hairy, compound leaf clusters were interspersed with small, bluish-purple flowers and, as the calf chewed on the offering, she drew closer to her mother and this too helped subdue the pain.

Within one moon, the swelling had subsided but the ordeal had left the tip of the young, tender trunk, deformed, scarred, and more awkward to use. It would take time for the calf to re-adjust to her impediment. The incident had left her resolute and she knew what she would do when she was big and next saw one of those slithering things. Her footpads would be big enough then.

As the earth turned, allowing dawn to ease its way into the elephant's lives, a very active male paradise-flycatcher woke the calves with its nervous and high-pitched, *Scratch, scratch, you little imp, you. Scratch, scratch you little imp, you.* Mabitsi looked up and wondered how the rust-coloured bird with such a long tail could be so busy, so early in the morning.

Mabitsi's half-sister bounced out of her dreams and onto all four feet, looking around for the snake. She trumpeted and moved closer to her mother. She didn't want to think about it any more.

The elephants moved northwards after a refreshing drink. The older animals carefully shepherded the calves to the safety of the centre of the herd. The Matriarch knew instinctively where to go. It would be a relentless march north, towards the Hill of Hope, once they passed the baobab.

9

Limpopo is born

1 year or twelve moons after the birth of Mabitsi

Limpopo the elephant was born in a glade near a stand of rough, dark-stemmed tamboti trees, a few hundred metres from the heavily-wooded Levubu River, which cuts a boundary across the far northern reaches of the Kruger National Park. He descended into the world on a dry summer evening, just as the earth moved to offer a glimpse of the full moon over the skyline. Limpopo was the calf of the Matriarch of the herd, the cow who walked with a slight limp. His father, who had one tusk and was the offspring of Mafunyane, had passed by the area twenty-two moons previously.

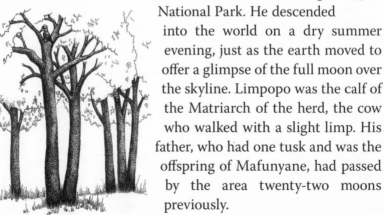

As Limpopo struggled to his soft feet, assisted by several of his aunts, his tiny trunk dangled out of control from his little elephant head. He blinked while trying to remove small slivers of birth tissue which still partially obscured his vision. His trunk flicked back and forth while seeking some resolution to his partial blindness.

A small flock of double-banded sand grouse had flown in for their evening drink. The males each sponged a teaspoonful of water into their breast feathers, for their helpless thirsty chicks crouching expectantly in the dry scrubland a ten-minute flight away. As the birds assembled at the water's edge they chatted amongst themselves, *Get in, it's horrible, get in, it's horrible.* They drank, soaked and were gone, bulleting away as though on a mercy flight.

More confident now, Limpopo suckled contentedly on his mother's left breast, as he reached up from between her stout front legs. The warm milk nourished him, making him aware of his family.

The two young bulls, Limpopo and Mabitsi, would grow up as first cousins without the knowledge and relevance of their own separate existences, and without knowing that their paths would cross under extraordinary circumstances.

The young bull calves were bright and alert.

Both Limpopo and Mabitsi's grandmother elephants had frequented the Shingwedzi area of The Park many moons before, and had had numerous wonderful, though short, relationships with a magnificent bull named Mafunyane.

Elephants in all regions recognised Mafunyane by his extraordinary long tusks. He had a gaping hole on the top of his head from some dreadful encounter in his youth. The cavity reached down into his sinuses, causing him discomfort and making him generally disagreeable. Mafunyane's massive, bulky frame had gained him the respect of all the bull elephants and fertile cows in the northern regions of The Park, and so Limpopo and Mabitsi had a confidence about them that set them apart from their peers. It was in their bloodline, imbuing their family with powerful leadership genes.

If there was something to be investigated, Limpopo was the first in line. As a result the Matriarch with the slight limp was continually disciplining him. But she knew how to balance the calf's activities, as she was teaching a future leader all about elephant behaviour.

The Matriarch stood quietly, browsing and listening to her son, Limpopo, at play. A noisy group of six Red-billed Woodhoopoes swayed ecstatically back and forth in a seesaw motion on the branch of an African Wattle. The iridescent navy blue and white birds, with their shiny green heads and slightly curved red bills, had moved into the tree in a straggling procession. The characteristic high-pitched cackling was started by one and taken up by the others to produce a cacophony of hysterical laughter similar to, but more musical than, that of Arrow-marked Babblers. The descriptive Afrikaans name of katlagters – laughing cats – is most apt.

The Matriarch felt a deep sense of contentment listening to the sounds of the forest around her, while observing the younger elephants. She was recording subconscious recollections of her surroundings, absorbing the many infrasound conversations taking place between three independent family groups of elephants, many kilometres apart.

The Matriarch and her family were about to move onto the open plain. They had completed their early morning bathing and had moved up and out of the river bed. She stood in the shade of a tall sausage tree. Numerous huge, light brown, salami-sized fruit hung down from the branches like multiple pendula of a vast leafy clock. The dark green canopy produced dense, cool shade for the elephants. The tree was succulent and the older animals browsed on the lower limbs as they rested, sucking and savouring the nourishing sap from the tender branches. They rolled the limbs and twigs between their molars, masticating and then swallowing the soft bark while dropping the shiny white twigs to the ground.

The Matriarch noted the density of the riverine forest. She gazed across the plain, recording individual landmark trees in the distance. She stored the memory of the dense groves of mopani scrub interspersed with marula and knobthorn trees.

She would return to this spot after the rains came and the nights were cooler. The mopanis held their leaves for longer after the rainy season, and remained highly nutritious well into the cold moons.

The Matriarch noted that, resulting from the heavily wooded plains, there was less tall grass in the area and therefore considerably fewer antelope and zebra. She wondered where they all were. There were only scattered herds of impala, wildebeest and the magnificent sable. Kudu were quite plentiful and felt secure amongst the more dense scrub and trees that dominated the veld.

Another message came through on the airwaves, confirming the presence of a family group of elephants not far off. She felt at ease and intuitively acknowledged and felt the presence of other offspring of Mafunyane. As she remembered him, she looked down at her son, Limpopo. There was an air of peaceful acceptance, that the wilderness was balanced and that this harmony offered the elephants a certain confidence and contentment.

There were though, from time to time, disturbances in the elephants' passive world.

Great noisy steel birds with whirling wings would drone in from any direction and whole families of elephants would be crowded together and lie down in humble submission to loud explosions. These families were never seen again and once when the Matriarch had visited a sight of all this fuss and noise, there were faint, disturbing signs of elephant blood on the soil, leaving her confused. She would quickly draw her family away and would not discuss these matters with the young calves.

The Matriarch could not fully comprehend all of this, and her days were soon once again taken up with her duties towards her families. She was quite a young, though very proud, leader.

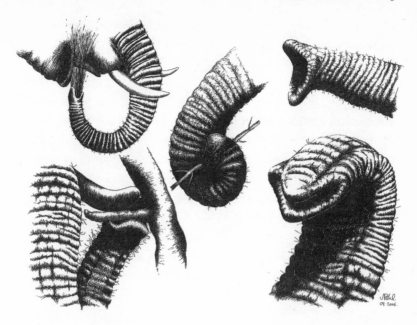

And so Limpopo spent the first twenty-four moons of his life being gently nursed by his mother. His days were spent playing with his friends, swimming, dust-bathing and romping in playful elephant style.

Every moment of every day of Limpopo's young life was filled with amazement. He and the other calves stayed close to the security of their mothers and their families. The young elephants watched with fascination as the older animals subconsciously taught the younger members of the herd the many secrets of elephant family life.

The calves tasted foliage that the adults ate, showing their own preference for the various young green branches and shoots of different trees and shrubs. They observed how the senior members of their family excavated bulbous, succulent roots and tubers from beneath the surface of the soil, and they followed suit. The calves watched and perfected the dexterity of their own little trunks, daily accomplishing the art of twisting, turning and manipulating their most valuable appendage in combination with their front legs and footpads.

Limpopo watched his mother as she held, with one foot, a fallen branch which blocked her passage and kicked the secure end with her other leg, severing it from the main stem. He tried this and almost lost his balance. He waved his trunk around with embarrassment while looking round to see if any of his friends had seen him. Then he tried again and to his surprise, it worked. He felt better!

One day, when he was twenty moons old, Limpopo decided to push down his first tree. He had watched one of the older bulls in the herd, who had a broken tusk, leaving it sharp and curved like a machete. The bull was an expert.

Limpopo had practised this tree-pushing-down once or twice, but it hadn't worked.

The herd had wandered onto a bank of clay soil and into a dense, closely-spaced forest of tree wisterias. The blue-to-mauve pea-shaped flowers hung in long cascades, like bells in a fairy's garden.

Limpopo had a sore stomach and had once seen the Matriarch push over one of these trees and excavate the roots which she had eaten during a time when she appeared to be trumpeting more than usual from under her tail. The young elephant, making sure that none of his friends were watching, pressed his forehead against one of the smaller trees in a cluster. The tree bent forward in submission to his strength. Limpopo was delighted. He pushed harder. The tree bent forward. Just then he lost concentration for a moment as he looked to see if, in fact, anyone was watching how clever he was. The thin tree slipped off his forehead, lashing sideways across his face and ears and against his upper foreleg, whipping and scraping along the side of his stomach.

The force with which Limpopo had been pushing caused him to lurch forward, lose his footing and crash headlong between two other closely-growing wisterias. His legs ended up tucked underneath his body, his trunk cast out in front of his head with his round rear end protruding above the green grass. His tail went straight up in the air in an attempt to counter-balance his fall.

There he lay, trapped, indignant, and unable to budge.

The Matriarch swung around at the noise and gently lifted her son from his embarrassing predicament. She curled her trunk around the tree and tore it out of the red clay soil, roots and all, and laid it next to where her son stood. Limpopo browsed on the succulent roots and soon felt better. No more would be said about this incident and the young bull calf resigned himself to wait until he was a little older before resuming any further tree-pushing activities.

He loved his mother so much more for her support. That evening when he suckled on her breast he rumbled thanks and gratitude to her. His mother was the best and she was the Matriarch, and this made Limpopo feel important.

Under her leadership, the members of the herd were sublimely content and secure.

Limpopo grew. He had his second set of molars. He was weaned and browsed contentedly on the succulent red flowers of the flame creeper, staying within reach of his mother, who remained ever protective of her two calves, just as she cared for and guided the entire herd. But troubled times lay ahead.

Even as the Matriarch dealt with the day-to-day events that made up their elephant existence, she knew that somehow she would have to lead them all to the precious reserves of water stored deep within the Hill of Hope. Would she remember where it was, when the time came? She knew that she would have to rely on a combination of the ancient knowledge passed down to her by her own elephant ancestors when she was a tiny elephant calf herself, and the intuition that would come to her aid when the crescent moon was visible. The Matriarch would have to put her Jacobson's organ to its most vital test. Then she would know the time was right: she would know which way to lead her herd to the Hill of Hope.

JPohl
28·08·2006

10

Letaba causes an accident

3 years or 36 moons after the birth of Mabitsi

Within four days, the elephants crossed the dry, stony river bed, and there stood the great baobab tree of myth and legend. Mabitsi moved to safety beneath his mother's soft grey belly, just in case one of those awful mice came out of the hole in the tree.

He closed his eyes in case he saw the horrible night birds with big eyes. He held on tightly to his mother's tail, stumbling along behind her for what seemed like an eternity, blinded by fear.

He did on one occasion open his right eye to peep at the tree. To his relief it looked like one huge, beautiful elephant leg; grey, secure and friendly. He rather liked the tree and all the birds that might live there. And the partially obscured black rock was there. Mabitsi thought it was all just wonderful. Then he closed his eyes just in case he saw one of those dreadful mice.

The herd had rested for a while, waiting for nightfall and the appearance of the crescent moon. This would assist the Matriarch to obtain guidance and direction for the journey north, to the Hill of Hope.

When the crescent moon was finally summoned by the rotating earth, the elephants, led by the Matriarch, moved off into the night. A Fiery-necked Nightjar shot up from the pathway in front of the lead elephant and fluttered timelessly in the evening sky, before coming to rest not far away and calling: *Good lord, deliver us! Good lord, deliver us!* As the elephants persisted at a steady pace, a fine cloud of brown dust rose from under their feet. There were fearful night sounds along the way, ones that Mabitsi had heard many times while lying securely under the protective body of his mother. On this occasion, though, they were on the move – more vulnerable, more afraid.

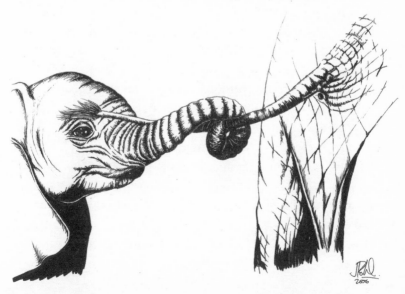

On the fringe of their journey were the shadows of those devilish, slope-backed hyenas. Their powerful jaws seemed to salivate in anticipation of an elephant meal. They too had pups to feed.

The cows and young bulls trumpeted incessantly at these suspicious-looking animals. It really seemed to have no effect on their menacing behaviour as they continued to skulk along in the dim light next to the trudging procession.

Mabitsi thought he should help, and nervously bugled at one of the hyenas. The peculiar sound caused one of the hyenas to change his step and arc sideways, merging into the darkness. There we are, thought Mabitsi, you'll see more of me when I'm big. This gave the young bull calf more confidence and he strode firmer in his footing and waggled his trunk with pride.

But the eerie drawn-out cackled wail of a black-backed jackal away in the distance caused the younger elephants to review their brave approach to the darkness, and they collectively huddled closer to their mothers.

When Mabitsi finally opened his eyes, it was quite dark and the herd continued to move forward relentlessly. The walking pace seemed to have increased in the cool of the evening and the small herd marched on through the dark, dangerous night.

As the earth greeted the sun, which illuminated the landscape on the morning of the first day after leaving the baobab, the Matriarch brought the herd to rest under the dense shade of a large, rounded, evergreen jackalberry tree, standing some thirty metres tall on the edge of the floodplain. The slender, drooping branches sheltered the elephants from the heat haze rising off the parched soil, and the younger members of the herd lay on the cool, leaf-covered alluvial sand under the tree.

The adults stood while feeding and fanned themselves with their ears.

Once evening approached and the air temperature dropped, the herd moved away, heading north in a slow determined procession. The elephants stopped occasionally to feed on acacia and mopani trees.

The night was cooler but remained eerie and sombre, the march relentlessly north-bound.

As the dove-breast grey of dawn illuminated the skyline on the second morning, the elephant family scrambled down the rocky bank of a dry river bed. The Matriarch remembered that in this river bed there was a large brown rock, half-submerged in the coarse sand. Beneath this boulder there might be water.

As the Matriarch and Mabitsi's mother approached the granite boulder they stretched their trunks forward, searching for clues as to where they should start digging. The surface-water had dried up.

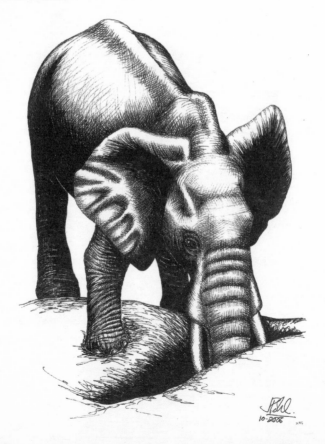

By systematically moving their front legs and footpads backwards and forwards, and shifting volumes of sand, the elephants began excavating a large hole under and next to the rock.

Although they toiled for two hours, there was no sign of any saturated sand.

By using her long, thin, creamy-white tusks, the Matriarch attempted to burrow beneath the rock. As the sand collapsed into the trench, the elephants methodically swept back piles of substrate.

An attentive Brown-hooded Kingfisher had taken up position on the rock, and darted back and forth into the excavation to retrieve an assortment of insect chrysalises, which lay in the cool, damp river-sand. The two elephants waved their front footpads at the bird as it landed.

With each captured morsel held securely by the bird's long powerful red beak, the kingfisher beat the insect against the rough stone, tenderising it prior to swallowing it whole. As the pupa slid down the throat of the blue-rumped bird, he held his head high with both eyes closed and gulped down his meal. After each successful plunder the kingfisher flapped his wings twice and called a loud dissenting, *Kik-kik-kik-kik me.*

From the shade of the Jackalberry tree higher up on the river bank, the patient younger elephants watched the bird's antics with amusement. By midday the strain of the combined effort of the adults was beginning to show. The miners were cooling themselves with their fan-shaped ears. The dark compact foliage of the tree cooled the river bank where the elephants stood, comforting them.

As the cavity expanded, the damp, musty smell of decaying driftwood, incarcerated deep within the profile of the finer sand well below the surface, caused the elephants to move up and out of the large hole for a breath of fresh air.

Letaba, one of the younger elephants, believing he may be of assistance, moved forward from under the tree. He positioned himself on the boulder and stood there, looking over the rock and into the excavation.

At that moment the rock began to move. His weight had shifted its centre of gravity, and in an instant the solid mass turned and tumbled over into the vast, moist cavern.

A younger cow that was helping with the digging was instantly engulfed under the mass of moving granite.

In a desperate attempt to recover his balance, Letaba rolled off his stiff legs and landed on his side. He threw his head back to try to secure anchorage from a branch of the jackalberry tree behind him. As he grabbed it, the branch snapped under the forward thrust of the moving elephant, sending the rock, the animal, and the limb of the tree crashing into the hole, engulfing the trapped cow.

As she tried to flee the falling rock, the damp river sand gave way under her footpads, preventing her escape. The boulder rolled sideways, trapping three of the younger cow's legs and bending and instantly snapping her spine. The breaking bones seemed to echo the sound of the cracked branch of the jackalberry tree, sending the rest of the small herd into retreat. The trapped animal released a terrifying scream and trumpet blast of agony.

A cloud of dust rose from the carnage.

The Matriarch turned to the scene of the accident to offer assistance. She cautiously approached the desperate animal while producing a series of solemn, deep rumbles and soft whimpers.

She was puzzling over how to assist. Her temporal glands exuded a sticky liquid, and there was the smell of fresh urine and dung in the air. A tear rolled down from her eye.

It was hopeless.

Hindquarter paralysis had set in, and the fate of the young cow was sealed in her sandy grave.

With a front leg digging at the river sand around her and her trunk waving desperately from side to side, the breathless animal eventually dropped her head onto the drying river sand. She was exhausted and helpless – and resigned to her predicament. Within an hour all signs of life disappeared. The pressure of the boulder on the trapped animal's diaphragm had drained the last breath out of her lungs and she mercifully slipped away as death engulfed her lifeless body. She lay on the river bed, with half of her body under the boulder.

The Matriarch gently touched the cripple with her front foot, eventually kneeling and draping her limp trunk over the young cow's head. She remained kneeling until she felt the final death shudder reverberate through the body of her niece, offering comforting rumbles, and touching the young cow's eyes with the tip of her trunk in order to close them.

Her dilemma was conveyed to the rest of the small herd through infrasound waves and the calves moved restlessly under the shade of the Jackalberry tree.

The young elephant Letaba, who had initiated the accident, stood some way off, shocked and embarrassed at his behaviour. He hadn't meant to cause all this grief and despair. His trunk hung vertically. It had been an innocent act of curiosity that had caused this tragedy. He produced a few soft fear trumpets. He closed his eyes.

The Matriarch stayed with the body of the young cow for some time. Her own temporal glands opened and a viscous liquid poured down the side of her face, staining the leathery indentations on her head as the moisture spread into the crevices between her eyes and her ear openings.

The shocked whites of her eyes showed, and she wept large teardrops which cascaded onto the dry river sand.

The Matriarch's body went limp in submission. She lifted her head and produced one long protracted social trumpet. The sun baked down on her body. When she eventually looked up, she noticed that the balance of the herd, with the exception of Letaba, were asleep in the shade of the tree. She lifted herself and moved up and under the canopy of the tree, looking up into its limbs, almost wishing to thank it for its assistance.

The Matriarch reached up and removed four or five mouthfuls of the nutritious blooms and leaves. She finally broke off a number of branches and placed them over the dead cow. When the body was almost invisible under the burial shroud, the Matriarch felt better and joined the rest of the herd.

As the earth saluted the sun, there was a *Let's go* rumble from the Matriarch, and the listless herd moved from under the large tree and headed out on their march north towards the Hill of Hope.

As the elephants reached the horizon, the Matriarch turned and lifted her trunk while facing down to where her niece's body lay. The low whooping call of a hyena distracted her and with a shudder and a head shake, she gathered the herd together by touching some of the calves, and they moved on into the night, assisted by another rumble.

11

The lions have their night

3 years or 36 moons after the birth of Mabitsi

By dawn of the following day Mabitsi, his two cousins and his half-sister were themselves nearly dead on their feet. They lay together between two large, lichen-covered boulders in a narrow gully under the canopy of a dense grove of riverbush willow trees.

Mabitsi's mother had liberated some soapy liquid from her bowel to feed her calves, giving them both instant relief. Mabitsi hoped that one day he would be just as resilient as his mother in times of crisis. They were all quickly asleep; their tiny trunks curled up safely, tucked in towards their little heads.

The small herd slept soundly through the intense heat of the day, their ears flapping rhythmically as they dreamed of the cool night walk, and the mystery of the water in the Hill of Hope.

In the early evening the herd roused themselves and moved out of the narrow ravine where they had spent the day resting.

The cows and the calves followed the Matriarch faithfully. They roamed along the ancient pathways, listening to the sounds of the African night.

While travelling along a section of open veld dotted with red termite mounds, two bold White-backed Honey Badgers scurried in between the elephants' footpads. They bared their sharp teeth at Letaba as he hugged close to his mother. The honey badgers had seen a large scorpion retreat under a hollow stump that the elephants had inadvertently rolled over as they walked. They rushed fearlessly between the many grey legs towering above them, turning the stump over and nipping the poisonous curved sting off the end of the scorpion's tail. They quickly devoured the arachnid, quite dismissive of the presence of the herd of elephants. Letaba was amazed at the tenacity and confidence of these busy silver and black animals. Who precisely did they think they were? Before the earth turned to greet the sun on the dawn of the third day, the exhausted herd was brought to halt by the Matriarch. Almost blinded by the dusty journey and with his dry pink tongue burning with thirst, Mabitsi came to a standstill next to his mother. Thick, white coagulation surrounded his eyes and his mother again wiped away the creamy fluid with her trunk.

Mabitsi's lungs felt congested as he struggled to breathe evenly. He wobbled on his four tired legs. There were no conversations amongst the adults as the Matriarch shuffled the younger cows and their calves together under the shade of a large Red-leaved Rock Fig, alive with fruit-eating barbets and louries.

As the earth greeted the sun, the Matriarch surveyed the landscape. She lifted her trunk high into the air and held it steady for a moment, the tip searching for the evidence she knew must be there. She lowered her trunk, inserting it into her clown-like mouth, pushing the tip firmly onto her upper palate and against two small holes in the lining of her jaw. As she gazed at the many hills to the north, she knew that ancient stored knowledge would assist her to decipher which one was the Hill of Hope.

Chemical messages shot lightning bolts of information into her lumpy elephant brain as her mind digested and interpreted the contents of the air. It computed and evaluated the information in a tiny fraction of the flick of an elephant's eye. The results were instantly stored, sorted and reacted upon.

Her trunk seemed glued to the inside of her half open mouth. She stood motionless and her huge, dusty legs appeared fixed to the slab of shale where she stood. The information that returned to enrich and empower her leadership was confused. This was not what her mother had briefed her on all those moons ago.

By looking around she reaffirmed that the shape and gradient of the approach was accurate, the herd having passed through an S-bend in the narrow gorge to the south of the Hill of Hope. For confirmation of the information stored deep within the reservoir of her memory, she raised her trunk above her head. This time she stretched it like a hose, high into the morning sky. She held her trunk in place, quite motionless, for what seemed like an eternity. She pleaded sincerely for a change in the first interpretation offered to her by her Jacobson's organ, as she again inserted her trunk firmly onto the two moist holes in the top of her palate. The herd was utterly and completely dependent on her knowledge and wisdom, and a cold breeze of doubt seemed to blow through her huge body, causing the short, stiff black hairs on her skin to stand up. Her blood seemed to flow cold as her ears pounded against her thick neck, and the pounding of her large heart almost dislodged her footing. The Matriarch swung round, searching the landscape for a possible error in her visual interpretation of the area. Eventually she stood still, gazing in confused denial at all those hills of hope.

Her mind appeared to shut down and while a feeling of complete desperation overcame her and her shoulders seemed to droop in despair, she produced just one pleading contact call.

From a state of anguish, ancient computed instincts led the Matriarch from where she stood to settle her back against a huge, uprooted tree-stump, excavated from the banks of the river by a torrent that had passed that way fifty-three moons before. She reversed the flanks of her dusty body and lodged them securely between the exposed roots of the stump. She knelt in humble submission to her exhaustion. The one outwardly curving tusk caused her head to rest at an angle, and there she fell into a deep sleep. The other elephants followed her example and there the herd lay, strewn haphazardly like huge discarded rubber mats on the floor of the wilderness.

Not far away, a family of inquisitive auburn dwarf mongooses popped their heads up from the various holes of the abandoned termite mound where they lived. The sounds of the Matriarch's shuffling, and the arrival of the elephants, had sent the little animals scuttling for cover in the safety of Mother Earth.

Only when they heard the consistent, rhythmic breathing that elephants produce when they sleep, did the mongooses have the confidence to re-emerge.

One by one, like a well-rehearsed puppet show, the small round-eared animals reappeared, their little heads moving excitedly from one side to the other.

Collectively, the group consisted of nineteen busy, chatty, little animals. The alpha female clearly had the say and nipped some of the younger members of her family firmly on their ears, as their boldness overcame their curiosity.

She called in extended squeaky grates while instructing her group, sounding like a poorly oiled hinge on the door of a garden shed.

Mabitsi's mother moved in her sleep, her rough skin rasping against the shale where she lay. Momentarily, the noise distracted the mongooses, causing two scouts to neglect their rear guard.

From high in the leafy canopy of a rough-stemmed leadwood tree, an alert Dark Chanting Goshawk saw his opportunity. Silently, his bright orange, featherless legs launched him from the camouflaged seclusion of his hiding place.

With his speckled head pushed forward, he dived away from his roost and torpedoed towards his prey, his nictitating membranes cleaning his eyes like miniature windscreen wipers on a Matchbox Porsche.

With extended talons, the goshawk hit a sub-adult male mongoose on the fringe of the distracted group.

On impact, the hind claw of his left talon penetrated the base of the animal's tiny skull. The front claws wrapped around the animal's face, piercing both eye sockets, instantly killing the young mongoose. The animal's brain exploded, shooting minute spurts of crimson blood out of each ear as the bird, now in full upward thrust, tried to extract the small dark, reddish body from the seclusion of the mound. The reaction of the little mongoose's body at the moment of impact was for its miniature paws to freeze in a death spasm, his tiny nails gripping the rough quartz crystals on the inside of the pink mound.

As the bird altered his angle of attack by drawing in his wings to lift the lifeless body of the mongoose into the air, he drew the furry little animal from the narrow earth chimney, elongating its slender frame. This thick elastic band appeared to stretch and then snap loose, assisting the goshawk in his upward climb.

The doors on a hundred garden sheds shut in alarm, closing in the remaining family members.

This noise didn't wake the Matriarch.

A Grey Lourie announced his belated warning to the mongooses, calling out in a resonating trill, *Go wayé, go wayé.* This noise didn't wake the Matriarch.

From within the tufts of spiky Cape Thatching Reed along the river bank, a Crested Francolin voiced his displeasure at the first kill of the day, as he walked without changing his

JPahl
30·08·2006

pace, remarking, *Very clever, very clever, very clever.* This sound didn't wake the Matriarch.

And then there was a reverberation, a sound more synonymous with the African bushveld than any other on the continent: a sound which stopped all creatures as they recognised it.

On this occasion, it began with a series of monotonous moans. At the end of each deep, tenured announcement, the tone of the sound crescendoed ever so slightly. The moan was repetitive and could be felt as well as heard. The notes rose onto the airwaves and floated upwind towards where the small elephant herd lay sleeping on the dry veld. The Matriarch's ears caught these loaded molecules of sound, guiding them towards the hairy openings on the side of her head.

The record of these awful sounds raced into the depths and innermost sanctities of her subconscious mind. She slept through the first bombardment of these fearful messages, but as her soul recorded the far-off sounds of the young black-maned lion on the plain below, there was a shift in her recognition. Ancient, intuitive warning bells began to ring deep within the recesses of her mind and her sleepy sense of alertness rose to a different level.

But the sound ceased and the elephants slept on, oblivious to the impending danger.

The fourteen members of Mabitsi's family slept soundly in their state of weariness and partial dehydration.

On the outskirts of the sleeping group was Mabitsi's half sister, the tip of her deformed trunk lying curled up next to her tired, feeble body. She was sound asleep like the rest of the herd. A cool, dry night-breeze blew gently over the elephants and into the valley below. Away on the outskirts of the plains, close to where the elephants had walked on the previous day was a pride of lions. Led by a particularly strong, young,

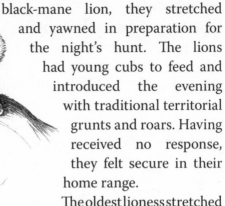

black-mane lion, they stretched and yawned in preparation for the night's hunt. The lions had young cubs to feed and introduced the evening with traditional territorial grunts and roars. Having received no response, they felt secure in their home range.

The oldest lioness stretched the full length of her lean body and yawned again. She moved off some distance from under the large Broad-pod Albizia, under which the pride had spent the last three days relaxing, playing and digesting their previous meal.

The tall thick-canopied tree grew on the arid sandveld. This was the centre of the lion's domain and the tree offered dense shade, giving the lions respite from the intense summer heat. The rough ageing stem and low branches near the base of the tree offered the cubs wonderful tree climbing, and the adults often rose up on their hind legs and scratched the thick main stem with their front claws, honing them for the next hunt. The tree was a busy place, as the creamy, white, round flower heads and reddish-brown seed-pods attracted birds and monkeys throughout most of the summer months.

With her head down, the lioness paused for a moment to sniff the air and the ground. There was a smell she hadn't encountered for some time. The tip of her tail flicked with excitement and as she lifted her head to gaze into the evening twilight she closed her eyes slightly, willing her stare to penetrate the dappled evening light.

Elephants had passed this way not long ago.

She acknowledged this with a low repetitive drawn-out series of moans, informing the other pride-members that it was time to prepare for the hunt.

The three-month-old cubs bounded up to playfully roll in mock-attacks as the two youngest males raised themselves on their hind legs to swat the tip of the lioness's tail. She chose to ignore them, concentrating on more important matters.

Another lioness, who was also suckling three cubs, moved up to where her companions stood and nuzzled against the older female's neck in submissive friendliness. The two lionesses moved forward, determination in their stride.

With the cubs secured in thick bush some way behind them and one sub-adult female left to look after them, the pride moved forward, stopping occasionally to listen and scent the air.

Having walked at a steady pace for an hour the pride suddenly stopped, drew together and then spread out in the crouching position. Each adult set themselves a short distance apart. They were alert and highly strung.

Darkness had drawn in and, other than the diesel engine call of the Mozambique Nightjar on the evening breeze with its incessant *Grrrrr, rrrrr*, the night was silent.

The lions lay and listened for some time pondering their attack, for, not far ahead, they knew there were elephants sleeping.

A female Spotted Eagle Owl called a solemn *Who, who's out there, who, who's out there?* One of the lionesses uttered an intense, low, almost inaudible moaning instruction and the other females, together with the two males, moved forward. The sleeping Matriarch shuffled uneasily where she lay.

The lions lunged forward, charged with energy and purpose. Their ears were pressed back against their heads and their tails flicked nervously with anticipation, balancing them as they ran. They approached the sleeping elephants from the west, where Mabitsi's half-sister lay, except that one of the lionesses had misjudged the scene and was, in the darkness, stalking a different sleeping elephant to the other members of the pride.

The lions all attacked at exactly the same moment. The lone lioness leaped straight onto the head of the Matriarch, who woke in an instant, raising herself from within the tangle of roots where she slept. Realising her error, the lioness released her grip and like a spring vaulted high above the rising elephant to land on her four paws and scurry away into the darkness.

This action was enough to divert the Matriarch's attention from the main attack and as she moved forward from the security of her retreat, one of the large dry roots of the dead tree where she had lain entangled itself under her right hip. She stumbled, losing precious moments.

The Matriarch produced a loud fear trumpet.

The other lionesses, in one harmonious movement, stormed forward and instantly pounced onto the front-end of Mabitsi's sleeping half-sister.

With the weight of five full-grown lions on her body, her predicament was hopeless. Unable to grip with the end of her deformed trunk, exhausted from her long trek, and in a profound semi-subconscious state while she slept, the elephant was taken by surprise. She released a terrified demoralised scream and a mournful wail, followed by a series of desperate trumpets. These, together with the alarm calls from the Matriarch, woke the remainder of the herd. Afraid and distracted, they fled into the night. One of the lions held onto the tip of the young calf's trunk to smother her. The large black-maned male bit into the elephant's neck below the under-jaw, and together they suffocated the desperate calf. She was only forty-one moons old.

Some distance away, the herd had regrouped and the Matriarch issued an attack rumble. Formed in a laager with the calves secured between the adults' legs, the elephants charged forward into the darkness in the direction of the commotion, but it was too late. The herd arrived on the scene where the flaccid and spent body of the young female calf lay and the lions scattered before them.

The Matriarch, assisted by Mabitsi's mother, knelt in an attempt to raise the dead calf. The other elephants, assisted by Mabitsi, Letaba and Klaserie, stormed the lions, trumpeting loudly while swinging their trunks forward in the hope of striking one of these awful beasts, but to no avail.

The lions moved away, then sat and waited. There was the smell of elephant dung and blood in the air. Eventually the aggressive lions muscled the weary elephants off and away from the carcass of the elephant calf. The Matriarch reeled with confusion and faced her dead daughter lying some way off. She listened as the lions fought to tear open the calf's thick hide; and she wept.

But her thirst and the needs of the herd outweighed the plight of her calf, and she wrenched herself away to deal with the task at hand. With a group rumble she motioned the cows to move the herd closer to the granite hills and once again stood alone in the translucent night sky, with her trunk held high above her head.

Where was the Hill of Hope?

12

A mysterious voice

3 years or 36 moons after the birth of Mabitsi

So Lord Rijhna had intervened and created circumstances by which the Matriarch would be forced to search at night.

On the African plains there is invariably a temperature inversion layer that occurs as the temperature drops in the evening, vastly improving the conditions under which low frequency infrasound waves travel.

Deep within the bowels of the Hill of Hope was a tiny stream of water pressured upwards by ancient tectonic forces. The stream cascaded down, over, and through the fissures of dolerite intrusions, reverberating against the caverns within the hill, sending delicate shock waves of attenuated sound through the hill, and up and out of a south-facing opening. This opening was camouflaged by a vast, overhanging granite cap beneath which families of San clansmen had sheltered many thousands of moons previously. These sound waves were caught on the wind and during sunny days were swept upwards, dissipating into the sky as they mixed with other sounds and the updrafts of warm air.

But at night the sounds and musty smells of this cavern condensed, hung in the air and were deflected from the inversion layer, returning to the surface of the earth after escaping from the entrance to the Hill of Hope. It was well past midnight.

At that moment the Matriarch extracted these signs and signals from the airwaves on the tip of her trunk, once again interpreting them through her Jacobson's organ. She had finally remembered that the entire exercise had occurred at night. As these memories came flooding back, she remembered being afraid while standing next to her mother, all those moons ago.

The Matriarch produced a deep and reassuring rumble. A series of knowledgeable tones and resonances, confirmed to the herd, her family, that resolution and hope were at hand. She gathered the elephants together with a motion of her trunk, touching all the calves on their heads as they walked past her. She inserted the tip of her trunk into the mouths of adult elephants, passing on the information she had received.

The elephants, following the Matriarch, moved along and up towards the broken and scattered hills. They formed a tight group of anxious animals, with Mabitsi, Letaba and Klaserie protected and secure between the older ones.

The moon, now five days following its crescent, assisted by showing them a passage through the rough terrain. They passed along and between the granite hills which were at a similar height to the bank above the ravine where Mabitsi was born. They trudged between the next four larger jagged hills and then the Matriarch stopped to rest the trusting and dependent herd.

Once again she snorkelled her trunk into the night air, searching for the whiff of confirmation she required.

The signals were stronger now, and as she listened she could hear and feel the gentle flow of the life-giving stream of water deep within the interior of the hill she knew was immediately in front of her. She produced a social trumpet which was answered by a series of rumbles. The temporal glands of two of the younger cows seeped with excitement and anticipation.

The cows milled around, lifting their front feet, seeking the additional confirmation they desperately required for themselves and their calves. A scops owl called in the distance, a repetitive, *Prove it, prove it, prove it.*

The frenzy grew and affected the calves. Klaserie pushed ahead, wishing to show his strength and resolve, but the orphan was tempered against his boldness in the dangerous night conditions.

Mabitsi and Letaba jostled and performed a short bugle duet to congratulate the Matriarch for saving their lives. They were exhausted.

A Red-chested Cuckoo announced the dawn, its repeated, *Piet-my-vrou, piet-my-vrou,* calling out from the canopy of shrubs on the hill, and a faint film of pastel grey light greeted the earth over the eastern horizon, beckoning in the day, full of hope and resolution.

The Matriarch remembered. She rumbled 'Stop,' to the herd. She stood and gazed, and as the world rotated to prepare a greeting for the sun,

the dawn light grew and there it was, an image being created before her eyes.

The high overhanging rock that camouflaged the entrance to the crevice that was home to the stream bore down on the elephants out of the dawn.

There was a gallery of rock art adorning the sides and ceiling of the overhang that was once the home to so many Bushman families. Strangely, there was the painting of a squirrel.

A small bowl had been created by the tiny stream, but it was only within reach of the elephants who were a hundred-and-fifty-six moons and older.

In preparation for her assent to test the water, the Matriarch moved forward and looked up at the ledge above. She turned and noticed the arrival of the first vultures at the killing place, and she was saddened.

As she took her first step on the final section of this journey to discover the Hill of Hope, the Matriarch heard a strange but recognisable series of group rumbles coming towards her from some distance away. Pleading, enquiring, infrasound contact and distress calls were interspersed with alarm bursts.

But there were other notes, rich in emotional content that shook the very fabric of her elephant soul.

There was one reverberation that was familiar. She searched her memory.

Who was the owner of this mysterious voice?

She lifted her front foot pad just off the rock on which she was standing. She lifted her trunk and as she turned, she opened her ears and listened once more to the cryptic messages reaching her from so far off.

And then she answered that elusive voice with a low-pitched roar, again and again. She initiated an identification roar, a confidence builder, followed by a contact rumble. And then she listened.

The rest of the impatient herd flapped their ears and the calves pleaded with suckle rumbles. Their thirst was desperate.

Her curiosity overcame her and, disregarding the appeals of her herd, the Matriarch turned and took one more step in the direction from which the contact calls had come, away from the Hill of Hope.

13

Finally, the Hill of Hope

3 years or 36 moons after the birth of Mabitsi

As she turned towards those amicable tones with her ears spread wide, she was confronted by a barrage of desperately thirsty elephants. Quickly realising that compliance was the order of the day, the Matriarch returned to her duties, acknowledging that the rest of the cows and calves were losing patience as they pressed her with a series of bellows and Let's-go rumbles.

The Matriarch stepped further up the rocky incline of the Hill of Hope towards the ledge below the overhang. On reaching the ledge, she knelt. Her back legs were a metre-and-a-half below her front legs, causing her back to arch, compounding her discomfort. She dangled her trunk over the opening and down into the crevice beyond where she could see.

Three Horseshoe Bats flew out as her trunk brushed against the roof of the cave. As they flew they released a series of high-frequency inaudible radar signals which helped them to navigate past the elephant's head and out into the open

air. Frightened, the Matriarch lurched back for a second. She again reached over and down into the darkness, searching for the water in the granite bowl on the inside of the cavern, where she could sense the sweet liquid. When she had first been there all those moons ago, she had herself been a calf and watched her mother perform this task.

She reached to the side of the opening and then she felt and heard a splash. The water was cold and pure. She sucked desperately with her trunk, trying to fill it in an instant, but the bowl was too shallow. She waited for the tiny stream to replenish the vessel, and sucked again. She extracted her full trunk, inserting it into her whiskered mouth. She poured the sweet, Hill of Hope water into her open mouth and down her dry, gaping, throat. As the water flowed down her gullet and gushed into her gut, it was immediately absorbed into her blood vessels, cooling and soothing her body. She closed her eyes as she relished the process. In the distance she again heard a recognisable greeting rumble. She repeated the drinking exercise a few times, giving her the strength to deal with other members of the herd.

The earth rotated, allowing the sun to move up and over the horizon and shine at an angle to where she stood. She shifted her body, allowing her to work in her own shadow. The other elephants were distracted and impatient. Mabitsi was first in the queue, having pushed and shoved his smaller frame ahead of the others.

Klaserie trumpeted at Mabitsi, who paid no attention.

The Matriarch again manoeuvred her trunk up and over the ledge, securing water by pinching closed the two fingers at the end of her trunk. She lifted her trunk up and out of the cavern while angling it down to where Mabitsi stood, now agitated beyond his ability to stand still. As the little elephant lifted his trunk back and over his head, his grandmother lowered her trunk and inserted its tip into the pink infantile opening of his mouth.

The water moistened his tongue and splashed against his tiny molars. It gushed into his throat and he gasped as it entered and cooled him. Mabitsi closed his eyes as he felt his body cool, and he thanked the Matriarch with a low, attenuated, muted bugle. By the time the three youngest calves had been watered, the Matriarch had developed a cramp in her left hip. She had stood in the same position – while stretching forward – for nearly four hours. With their thirsts quenched, the calves moved back.

Klaserie was still grumpy and jostled Letaba out the way, who was having none of it and bugled at Klaserie with contempt.

Mabitsi's mother, the cow with the torn left ear, took up the Matriarch's position after carefully listening to some instructive, vibrating rumbles from the one who knew best.

Having moved away from the Hill of Hope and with her thirst partially quenched, the Matriarch used her outward-curving tusk to move a huge stump into the shade of a tall Scented Thorn. The tree was in full bloom and the yellow flower-balls nourished her while the remainder of the elephants drank their fill.

While standing on a stump, the Matriarch stretched high into the upper canopy of the tree from where she had caught the fragrance of some of the previous season's pods. The pods were a dark brownish-red colour, and their sweet scent caused the Matriarch to step down from her lofty position and buttress her head against the rough stem of the tree. By systematically moving to-and-fro, she shook the tree, and many of the pods floated down onto the sandy soil, like a hail storm on a windless day.

She gathered up the molasses-tasting pods to mollify her energy. It was at that moment that she once again felt and heard the infrasound waves resonating through the atmosphere.

She knew that sound! She searched her memory for a recollection.

And then there was a flash of memory. She remembered water, a gushing flooded river, but the memory blurred. The Matriarch called a greeting rumble. She opened her ears, turned her head and waited. She stood quite still; listening.

There it was again, although from a slightly different direction. The rumble was quite distinctive and in its high notes and tones, the Matriarch thought she felt a slightly different, more emotional answer to her previously pleading resonance, almost as though the call was being answered at a different level of perception.

Another flash passed through her. With her eyes closed, she imagined water gushing over her, engulfing her, sweeping her legs from beneath her. The memory came flooding back. She was a calf swimming for her life, pursued by men with guns. There was the blast that had caused her aunt to slump backwards and kneel. They were being chased. As the explosion came from behind them, she and her younger half-sister plunged into the swollen waters of the Mongezi River to escape the pursuit by a hunting party that had entered The Park from the north.

The floodwaters had engulfed her small, buoyant body, sweeping her downstream and away from her family. The water had washed over her half-sister's head, preventing her from breathing as she struggled to free herself. Her little trunk had been searching for the surface. At one point she stretched upwards and above the rushing, pounding deluge, allowing her to take a gasp of air and rumble a calf response to the roar of her mother. She remembered the scream and fear trumpeting of her half-sister who seemed trapped below the surging waters, and then there was silence.

She remembered opening her own eyes to the blackness of the noisy, boiling waves of the river. She remembered having bobbed about on the surface of the water for some time and being washed sideways, landing on a coarse rocky embankment at a place where the river turned to rush away.

She remembered scrambling up and between the sharp jagged rocks on the river bank, coughing and gasping for air. She was alive, alone, afraid and completely exhausted with fear and abandonment. Only then did the Matriarch recognise certain pleading tones from the elephant moving in her direction now.

Anguished by desperation and longing, all those emotions flooded into every crevice of her old and wise elephant body.

Could it be that, out here at the foothills of the Hill of Hope, she would be reunited with her half-sister?

With renewed confidence, she rumbled a distinctive trembling female-to-female call. Tears burst from her eyes and her temporal glands shot out streams of sticky liquid. In her excitement she urinated uncontrollably as she jogged forward past the carcass of her daughter, dispersing the vultures with multiple raucous trumpets. She charged between the trees of a small grove of mopanis, rumbling and bellowing as she ran. She lumbered on through a dense patch of sickle-bush, their thorny branches scraping and rasping her flanks.

The Matriarch bulldozed her way between and over a pile of fallen logs, sending a confused greenish-yellow mongoose into full flight, and after what seemed like an age, there, barrelling towards her with a similarly clumsy strut, was another elephant. This large female had an impediment in her walk and as she appeared from behind a small baobab tree, the Matriarch noticed that her half-sister had an obvious limp.

How had she been injured? As the two adult elephants met, the atmosphere was charged with warmth. Their eagerness resonated through the air. Simultaneously, their temporal glands burst into action, sending solid streams of sticky liquid cascading down their cheeks.

Recognition was immediate and without question.

They mouthed each others' Jacobsen's organs for confirmation. They urinated gallons of yellow liquid for further verification. The Matriarch with the outward-curving tusk disgorged a trunkful of soapy liquid from her gut to slake her half-sister's dire thirst. The two animals rubbed each others' sides and produced deep greeting rumbles, sounds of contentment and relief.

For three days they were inseparable. The atmosphere was filled with the joy of being reunited. On the fourth morning the Matriarch with the slight limp formally introduced her son, Limpopo, to Mabitsi, Letaba and Klaserie. Limpopo was a little intimidated by Mabitsi, and rushed forward at him, with his trunk swaying from side to side in a display of dominance. Klaserie remained aloof, whooshed a bit, and walked away to be alone. How he missed his mother, particularly when all the other calves felt so secure. Letaba felt uncomfortable, as he had a swelling on his right hip which was slightly septic. (A sharp thorn from a sickle bush had entered the skin one night while he slept on a shrub dried out by a bush fire.) He moved to favour his left leg and fanned himself. The calves mouthed one another, and rumbled and bugled as their confidence grew.

The two matriarchs kept each other company; touching, rubbing and rumbling with a closeness neither of them had previously experienced. What conversations they were having and what information their trunk-mouthing was imparting, the remainder of the herd would never fully comprehend.

The two females, who had settled for the night some distance from the carcass of the decaying young female calf, sauntered down at dawn the next day and together chased away the hyenas and jackals. They spent the morning packing freshly broken branches from the scented thorn tree, high and comprehensively, to cover the remains of their daughter and half-niece.

During this time there was silence between the two wise elephant cows. There seemed to be a deep, inner understanding and they nurtured the additional bonding that the burial ceremony offered them. Occasionally during their vigil, as they passed one another, they would stop, lay down their loads and touch heads, eyes and ears, almost to reassure each other that they were together again.

The scavengers stood some way off, observing the two elephants as they worked. Huge flocks of vultures soared on thermals of hot air and others roosted on the trees surrounding this graveyard in the wilderness. The Lappard-faced Vultures had been the first to arrive after the lions killed the young elephant cow. With their powerful beaks the huge raptors had initiated the opening up of feeding areas through soft areas of skin on the animal. The Hooded and White-headed Vultures had followed the White-backed Vultures, tearing deeper into the carcass.

The burial task was completed as the earth rotated, placing the sun at its highest point.

An impenetrable barrage of heavy, thorny cover had been placed over the body of the young calf. The two cows stood for a moment and then shook their heads while looking down at their morning's work. The great expanses of their ears resounded with energy and dryness. Dust rose from their heads and drifted away on the midday breeze. This was a job well done and at last Mabitsi's grandmother was able to rest; she had done her duty. The last rites ceremony was completed with a snort and a final indignant bellow at the vultures.

Having stood for a short while prior to leaving the scene, the Matriarch reached through the thorny barrier with her trunk for one last time and touched her daughter's head at the base of the trunk, where the tiny tusks protruded. The two cows moved away without a sound.

The united herds spent three additional moons in the area, close to the water source in the Hill of Hope, regularly quenching their thirst. At one point Mabitsi and Letaba, who remained inquisitive about this place where the adults drew water, ventured up the side of the Hill of Hope. Mabitsi clambered onto the ledge with his front legs and peered into the dark cavern. He couldn't see any water and was about to venture further when there was a trumpet blast from the Matriarch. A danger rumble followed and the two calves retreated in haste, scurrying between the legs of the adults to escape any further scolding.

The elephants shared the water with a troop of Chacma Baboons that had stayed on in the district to benefit from the Hill of Hope.

The three elephant calves, Mabitsi, Letaba and Klaserie, were growing to know and accept their new cousin Limpopo, and spent some of their play-time seeing whether they could trap one of the alert baboons in the Hill of Hope while it was sneaking a drink. The baboons, though, constantly outwitted the calves.

The rains were very late. The veld had shrivelled and was waiting.

One morning the wind direction changed and the air was cooler. It was blowing from the south-east and clouds had gathered during the night. By mid-morning the strength of the wind had risen, and a dense bank of moist, frontal clouds moved over the area, cooling the landscape. As night fell and the air pressure dropped, the clouds condensed and by midnight a fine rain started to fall. It woke the elephants, who relished the moisture on their dry skins.

By dawn of the following day the intensity of the rain had increased and there were sounds of thunder in the distance. The storm moved closer as the morning wore on and tremendous lightning and thunder preceded a deluge of rain unseen in the region for many moons.

Small streams came alive to replenish larger rivers, and pools formed in depressions in the rock formation and the soil.

The two Matriarchs felt an enormous sense of relief. Early one morning they rumbled a very purposeful *Let's-go* murmur and together the two herds, now united in friendship, moved

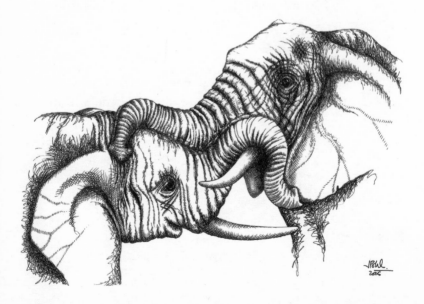

off slowly, heading south. They travelled in a procession past the now entirely decayed, bony carcass of the young female calf who had succumbed to the lion's attack. As each elephant passed the dry corpse, they turned and gave one last head shake, or trunk lift or wave, each according to their own expression of grief and condolence.

As Klaserie passed he stood for a moment and a tear rolled off his rough cheek. He remembered the death of his own mother. He then moved forward while giving one slow, mournful extended grief rumble. Then he fainted playfully at a passing field mouse.

The elephants moved on and away, heading south to their traditional home range.

The last elephants to pass were the two matriarchal half-sisters, one holding the other's tail. They hoped they would never need to return to this sad place, or ever have to search for the Hill of Hope again. There was a low duet rumble as they passed by without stopping.

The Tree of Life appears

4 years or 48 moons after the birth of Mabitsi

As the appointed custodian of all the elephants in the world, the elephant god and the god of prosperity, Lord Rijhna had worked on the master-plan for the wild herds of *Loxadontus africana* on the plains of Africa, developed by trial-and-error over thousands of moons.

He had guided and advised both elephants and humankind in a most sincere and well-intentioned manner.

As the sixtieth anniversary of Mabitsi's birth approached, and under his plan for the pre-ordained reduction of the elephant populations of the Kruger National Park, Rijhna found himself confused and unsure of the process. Trying to guide and orchestrate the annual elephant cull was weighing heavily on his conscience. In Asia he felt far removed from the events unfolding in Africa. The entire matter was beyond his reasonable jurisdiction, and for the first time the elephant god felt he required assistance, or even perhaps an African successor.

It was 1994.

This is the way folklore evolves and unfolds.

Lord Rijhna believed he should advertise the post. As he had the head of an elephant, he set about producing some very out of the ordinary request rumbles, a few trumpet blasts, a couple of lost rumbles and he even threw in a few roars for good measure. Rijhna continued in this vein for four moons without receiving a single response. Confused, he contacted many of his deity colleagues regarding this matter. First, he sought Cupid's opinion. Bad move, he was in love and a bit distracted.

Zeus was of course married to Hera and being the rain god and the god of justice and mercy, who punished the wicked, he didn't show much interest in Rijhna's problems.

Hades too, found little reason to sympathise with Rijhna, as he was the lord of the underworld ruling over the dead, and wasn't really interested in elephants.

Hermes was the cleverest of all the Olympian gods and, being the messenger to them all, suggested to Rijhna that he borrow his winged sandals and hat and race off to contact Lord Sivia, the destroyer of all evil and a fellow eastern god. He, together with Anamon who had the face of a monkey, proved to be of little help.

And then Rijhna remembered Lord Vishnu, a major Hindu god, the preserver of the universe and the prominent second god of the Trimurti. His origins lay in the fact that he was eternal, an all-pervading spirit, and associated with primeval waters that were omnipresent before the creation of the universe. Lord Vishnu congratulated Rijhna on his wise countenance and diligent search for a replacement African elephant god. Vishnu pledged his support and wished Rijhna well in his endeavours.

Lord Rijhna would have to alter his approach. What was it about Africa that solicited such a negative response? Clearly he would have to wise up on African cultural thinking and philosophy – and where else to gather all this information but through the www, the Worldwide Ways of Wisdom? So he accessed the deepest, most treasured sanctities of this web of intrigue.

He needed to solicit all the thinking the world had, and so he ordered the mythological-god book. This book contained no written text, no covers, rib or pages. It was a book of the mind. The book advised him to enter the spirit world high above the earth, a viewing platform, a vantage point in cold, thin air, from where he could obtain a more global perspective on his predicament. This place was acknowledged in deity circles, a place from where the energy would flow, and from within this psychic world, a replacement African elephant god or goddess would be selected and appointed. For this task Rijhna needed to mount an adventure, in a deep state of transcendental meditation with sufficient provisions for an extended, cold climate journey. He needed to return home.

Rijhna headed for the mountains, accompanied by a hundred carts drawn by cumulus elephants. There would be a fireworks display and thunderous base-toned music. It was once again the onset of the monsoons. He felt a bit like the elephant-piper as he ventured north into the heart of Nepal and beyond – to the Himalayas. People and elephants alike wished him well during his journey.

He ventured through deep canyons in the lower Annapurna Himal, over steep passes and across beautiful green and peaceful valleys. He navigated up river courses and under clear waterfalls through the Longtong region, up and beyond the tree line and into an environment of pure white snow.

He eventually settled on a slope where he saw Mount Everest. This was a clean place, where the air was thin and elephant thoughts would travel forever. A place where purity of spirit and intentions would abound. On the expiry of two moons, and having travelled over rough and difficult terrain, he reached his zenith. Rijhna sat on an incline facing west, where, through his imagination, he could see the shores of Africa. At his back was a sheer wall of ice. It reached up to the height of the tip of the outstretched trunk of an adult bull elephant. Here he prayed, with his trunk neatly curled up on his lap and with his pink-lined, grey ears open and receptive to the guidance he knew would be forthcoming.

Rijhna sought celestial guidance, searching the heavens. From the angle of the Polaris star and the position of the moon at midnight, he rumbled into the western sky. In his mind he travelled through the galaxies of time and space, probing for advice. In this meditating state, he elevated his entire being, high above the earth seeking resolution, pleading for transposition.

This period of his search lasted for a further two moons. There was no response.

And then one night, as our glorious earth rotated to greet the full moon and place it at its meridian above where Rijhna slept, he had a dream – an African dream. In the dream, the sun shone through a gap between the clouds over a dull, arid landscape, in the central region of Southern Africa, the Kalahari Desert.

The sun radiated amber throughout the wilderness. There were shades of yellow-stone, umber and tan. The dream reflected a wilderness scene which included a yellow ground squirrel and a golden-brown man. The short, wiry man with his sun-baked face gathered up his squirrel prize. As he turned, he inadvertently pressed a single, abandoned, black kidney-shaped baobab seed into a crevice in the dry, sandy earth. The seed was one of many shed from the velvety pod of an enormous lumpy, grey tree, which in some curious way, seemed fashioned from, and resembled the skin of an old elephant bull.

The seed would lie in wait for the rains to come.

As the lithe figure jogged away from this anonymous garden, he was joined in a dance being choreographed in his mind, which included surreal, four-legged beasts. These gentle monsters danced in the sky and bounded off the earth in celebration of some yet untold happening.

The dream scene then moved to where Lord Rijhna lay. The sheer wall of ice behind him was transformed into a rock face of dappled granite with a vertical crack running down its length. From the rock-face hung the roots of rock-fig and honey bees darted to and fro from the crevice.

On the flat rock below sat a girl whose skin was burnt yellow and dark amber, and who sang a soft melody. The young female voice resonated through the desert air, and it bore a message. It was a message of hope and resolution and seemed to offer Lord Rijhna some solace in his elephant thoughts.

Rijhna woke abruptly to see the vision of a tall black man standing over him, dressed in an array of spotted skins. His body was adorned with seashells and beads. As he moved, the adornments produced music as they swung from his powerful frame. On his head he wore a crown of long white and black ostrich feathers. Around his neck hung a string of charms with small bones, seedpods and seashells amongst them.

The man carried an ebony bowl with symbols painted on its exterior. On his wrists and ankles were puffs of seedpods and insect cocoons which whispered with soft, rattling sounds as he moved.

The mystery man announced that he was a sangoma from the African spirit world. The bowl that he held bore a calling from the Tree of Life, the most revered mythological deity throughout the African continent.

This Tree once pursued Mma, the great mother goddess, who had created herself in human form from the eternal spirit, Unkulunkulu. Mma had in turn created the stars, the sun, the earth and later the moon. Although immortal, the goddess Mma was cursed with strange desires and feelings, which man and beast would inherit. Mma complained of her loneliness while creating the universe, and pleaded for a companion.

Early one morning, as the toothed range of hills known as Mount Taba-Zimbi turned to welcome the first rays of the sun, a voice beckoned. Her response was immediate, as she sought a mate. Mma sauntered over to meet her caller, but was shocked and repulsed by the all-embracing entanglement of crawling, living roots scrambling over rocks in pursuit of her.

'Come, my beloved! Come to me!' roared the Tree, drawing the goddess close, and with his rock-studded mouth he bruised her silvery lips with a kiss. 'I am the Tree of Life – your mate – and I desire you!'

The terrified goddess fled, travelling north. The couple eventually reached a bleak wasteland later to be known as Ka-Lahari. Here the goddess plunged headlong into the Lake

Makorikori, streaking through the waters like a luminous fish – but still the Tree of Life followed her.

In a final effort to escape, Mma rose through the surface of the water and flew like an owl into the night sky. The Tree of Life was left behind, wading through the mud.

Finally, the Tree of Life, in a sudden flash of inspiration, scooped up a double handful of rocks, clay and sand from the bottom of the lake. He rolled them into a huge ball, larger than Mount Kilimanjaro, and with one lash of his branches, he hurled this formidable missile skyward at his love, who was by now almost at the stars.

The ball flew upwards and dealt a blow to the goddess on the back of her head. As she plunged earthward, limp and unconscious, towards her mate's waiting arms, the ball rebounded and tumbled into orbit, where, through its radiance, it still regulates the loves of men, beasts, birds, fishes and the time clock of the elephants; and the moon was born.

Years after her capture the goddess felt movement inside her and she counted the stars just as Lord Rijhna did while in the Himalayas, listening to the sangoma.

After a thousand years of birth-pangs the goddess delivered a nation of human beings, who spread in their multitudes to populate the bleak Ka-Lahari. They are referred to as the !Kung people.

Meanwhile, the strangest change had come over the Tree of Life. Green buds burst from his limbs and clouds of seeds billowed from him and fell upon the earth. They established roots on the rocks and sand. Soon a lush carpet of green was creeping over the earth. Plains of undulating grass and dense forests were established on the landscape.

The Tree of Life bore living, howling, snarling animal fruit. From his branches they fell to the ground and scuttled off into the forests in their millions. From cracks in the trunk of the Tree of Life birds of all kinds flew, filling the air with their love-calls. There were ostriches and ibises, eagles, hawks, flamingos and sunbirds; the birds we know today as well as others which we've never seen, like the two-headed talking Kaa-U-La birds, the holy ones which we know about only from legends, soared in the sky.

From the roots of the Tree of Life swarmed reptiles of all sorts and shapes, as well as clouds of insects rising into the air in continuous streams.

Soon the earth resounded with the voices of life, songs which still resonate but which may one day trail away into oblivion, leaving only the nothingness which was there before. 'Beware. The elephants are not responsible,' cautioned the sangoma.

High above the earth on the snowy incline where Lord Rijhna was camped out, awaiting an answer from the shores of Africa, the Tree of Life had reappeared in the guise of the sangoma.

Still clutching the bowl, the sangoma assured Rijhna that many general councils had met in the mountains and on the plains of Africa, over a period of many moons.

Rijhna's early pleading rumbles had not been ignored, but issues of this complexity required careful countenance to ensure the correct resolutions. There had been an indaba. This indaba, had, in African style, started late, hence the delay in their reply. The indaba was pleasantly disorganised but, 'Here I am. We needed to refer these matters to the Shades,' concluded the sangoma, 'And we have an elected replacement elephant goddess to do your work.'

This new African elephant goddess was appointed, moulded and trained with the guidance and assistance of the Tree of Life. The African elephant goddess, who is the daughter of *ubuntu*, will be known as Mma-Thohoyandou (pronounced Toy-an-doe): mother with an elephant's head. Mma-Thohoyandou will be the goddess of biodiversity, the goddess of gender diversity and the goddess of reason, and will be given the custodianship of all the elephants in Africa. She will reside at her royal kraal in the Limpopo Province in South Africa, in an area known as Venda. The kraal is simply referred to as Thohoyandou. At her inauguration Mma-Thohoyandou will draw on the ancient wisdom of the African Tree of Life to guide her in this honourable task: the custodianship of all the elephants in Africa.

Mma-Thohoyandou's companion is a female desert meerkat. The meerkat denotes alertness, and an acute caring sense of family. She is the protector against aggression. Africa was ready and prepared to relieve Lord Rijhna of his duties and to take on the responsibilities it knew it had to; for and on behalf of the elephants, their human companions and the biodiversity itself. And the philosophy was simple. '*Go kaone go dira dilo le le seboka go phala go dira selo o le tee.*' It is better to do things together rather than as an individual.

From the summit of the Soutpansberg Mountains (the Mountains of Salt) Mma-Thohoyandou will deliberate on the elephants' future in Africa. Her view of the vast plains of Africa from her throne will be north – to and beyond the equator – and south, to the Cape of Good Hope. She will reach east to the warm Indian Ocean and her ears will listen in a westerly direction, over the deserts to the cold Atlantic Ocean. She will observe the elephants in all directions.

Mma-Thohoyandou will be noted for her compassion, her empathetic understanding of the ways of the wild, and for her knowledge of *ubuntu*. The principles of *ubuntu* will be institutionalised in the elephant debate with *mutingati* (biodiversity) as the primary consideration. Mma-Thohoyandou will be respected by elephants and people, in the African way.

Standing with his bare feet elevated slightly above the snow, and in a halo of light, the sangoma levitated into the night sky. The moon caused his skin to shine and eyes to sparkle. The charms and shells adorning his body resounded with music in a jingling-symphony as he moved in celebration of the resolution; and then he was gone. Lord Rijhna lifted his head with his trunk in an upward curl as he saluted the occasion, and in his celebratory rumble some of the accompanying Sherpas thought they heard the now-retired elephant god Lord Rijhna say, in Tibetan, '*Soo soo la gyalo!*' The gods are triumphant!

Mma-Thohoyandou has the head of an African elephant with beautiful evenly curved cream-coloured tusks, and the body of a wiry, lithe human female form. Her wrists and ankles are adorned with sets of strung insect cocoons. The caterpillar of the Green Lunar moth which feeds on the leaves of the marula tree, grows to maturity, plump and with honourable intentions. The worms extract delicate, silky threads from minute spinneret glands on the sides of their heads. They expertly spin a tough cocoon around their bodies and seal it from within. Once the task is completed the now fully mature caterpillar lies quite still, and one of the great miracles of nature unfolds.

Within a few days the larva undergoes a metamorphic transformation and becomes a chrysalis or pupa. It lies dormant, incarcerated and secure. In the spring of the following year, the pupa stirs and a further refinement of the evolution of metamorphosis occurs. A moth emerges from its secure and secret hiding place within the silk cocoon. Once free, the moth stands quite still, pumping fluid into its wings in preparation for its maiden flight.

These robust, empty cocoons are collected and filled with tiny stones and bright red seeds from the lucky bean or sacred coral tree. The ends of the silky tubes are sealed and sewn together to form bracelets, which create their own rattling accompaniment of musical synthesis as the body of the elephant goddess moves.

Around her neck is a necklace of small cowrie-shells smuggled through Crook's Corner, having been collected from the coastal beach sands of Xia Xia on the Mozambique coast. A leopard-skin loin-cloth adorns her waist, covering her groin and buttocks. The elephant goddess will hold a staff or wisdom stick in the shape of a fly whisk, cut from the branch of a mopani tree. She bears a clay bowl of marula beer. A leather bag containing wild, indigenous seeds, quartz crystals, animal bones, small feathers and tufts of hyena fur, will rest at her feet.

Lord Rijhna was asleep on his back in a cart lined with grass and bamboo fronds, distracted by a wave of elephant thoughts. He leaped up as the glare of the sun reflected off the snowy peaks.

The party packed their belongings and moved down the mountain. As they descended they were blessed and encouraged by the local country-folk who sang and danced in the knowledge that Lord Rijhna would now be more fully focused on matters of purely eastern concerns. Rijhna waggled his trunk; there was a skip in his step and his temporal glands opened, allowing a thin, sticky substance to be exuded; he had done his job. It was now time for relaxation and enjoyment. His eyes sparkled and as he opened and spread his ears he produced a deep guttural pulsation; a musth rumble. The upper front section of his head vibrated visibly and then he sat up and froze in anticipation, with his ears spread wide. He listened for a response and – just for good measure – he politely urinated on his legs as he rolled off the cart and glided ahead of the procession.

There were ten black ravens soaring above this happy cumulus procession.

15

Klaserie's dust storm

4 years or 48 moons after the birth of Mabitsi

Mabitsi, Letaba, Limpopo and Klaserie – and not necessarily in that order – were inseparable. The calves had bonded into a cohesive band of brothers-in-arms. There was no risk they wouldn't take and no trick they didn't play. The calves simply ruled the combined herds. They were bright enough, though, as all young elephants are, to know how much they still needed to learn. They listened and observed intently, to what the adult elephants thought, rumbled and achieved. There were ideas to be grasped regarding every aspect of elephant life – where to walk, how to find and know what plants to eat, who in the natural world was dangerous and why one should not pay the slightest attention to zebras who spend most of their days kicking, burping and farting out loud in public. It was strange how some animals wore their pyjamas even during the day.

A porcupine was certainly not someone to mess with. When you're still a small elephant, do not venture into deep water

until you significantly outweigh those sinister crocodiles. And furry, striped skunks stink if you annoy them.

So the calves grew in stature and wisdom. Their family was their security. These young elephants were from a powerful elephant bloodline.

The only time elephant cows disciplined the calves was in the face of danger – to themselves or the herd in general.

The journey south, away from the Hill of Hope, had been leisurely, alternating between grazing and browsing.

The grass was lush and coming into seedhead, and the elephants were able to harvest great swathes of the various types. The calves were taught how to recognise which grasses to select as they meandered through the veld. They curled their trunks around a number of grass stalks and leaves and bundled them together. With one well-timed pull, the tuft was removed, either with the roots and a clod of soil attached, or neatly cut off just above ground level. With a soil ball attached, the elephants then had two choices: either they fed the tuft into their mouths with the soil hanging just outside their hairy lips, and then neatly severed it, or they beat the soil ball against their front legs.

Certain soil types produced sweet, more palatable grasses. More mineral-rich grasses would establish themselves in sodic soils. Tall Panicum grasses grew near the river banks and set rich, tasty seedheads. The sight of the tall *Panicum maxicum* stands of grass would send the calves jogging comically ahead to reach them first. In the river beds the reeds were softer and sweeter at the onset of the rainy season, when the heat of the sun nurtured the stems causing them to elongate, making them pliable and succulent. And along the river banks, if one arrived first and sought out the newly formed seedpods of the shaving brush combretum, then there were rich rewards of flavour.

On the clay soils away from the river, in the thorn veld, grew one of the elephant's favoured trees, the knobthorn. The bark on the stems of these tall, thorny trees was preferred to other trees, and the young elephants were taught that these were one of the best.

Klaserie, of course, preferred to be on his own, not participating in his friends' silly games; he tended to miss his mother. Lying alone one day, having browsed on the fleshy pulp of the wild mango tree, Klaserie reflected once again on the circumstances of his mother's death.

Klaserie had been quite young; in his eighteenth moon. The herd had spent a quiet night near a marshy area in the centre of The Park. At dawn the Matriarch had rumbled a calm and confident *Let's go*, as the young calves had been woken by a cold wind, blowing from the south. Klaserie was afraid and stayed quite close to his mother. The adults sought shelter from the icy blast.

After a short walk from the marsh, the elephants found themselves on high ground and in the centre of a small forest of brown ivory trees. The tall trees had established themselves on an elevated outcrop or mini-plateau of decomposing granite.

There was a thin layer of red soil, the remnants of an ancient termite mound, covering the area.

Many moons prior to this event, during the establishment of the wilderness, and possibly under the hand and guidance of Lord Rijhna, a proud mature elephant bull had deposited three large dung balls on this spot, while urinating his musth scent onto the mound.

The old bull had stood for a while on this east-facing mesa, searching the airwaves for an answer to his musth rumble on this bright spring morning. Within moments of the dung balls landing, dozens of dung beetles flew in in competition. They each prepared a ball in which to lay a single egg. The dung balls contained many mature seeds of the brown ivory

tree, the succulent flesh having been digested from around the hard casing. The seeds were moist, fertile and embalmed in a nutrient-rich package, ready for germination. The remnants of the dung ball lay scattered, mulching the seeds.

Following this process, a female Natal Francolin, while busying herself with her brood of six fluffy brown chicks, had scratched in the dung remnants, scattering and dispersing each seed to its own resting place. A few of the seeds rolled into cracks in the dry soil.

Over a period of moons, the traffic, wind and dust created by the passage of time in the bushveld covered the seeds. A fine garden of mixed grasses established itself on the soil, leaving the brown ivory seeds secure, fertile and waiting. After the passing of fourteen moons and the onset of the following rainy season, the clouds gathered one afternoon. The violence and energy charged the heavens into an atmospheric war zone. Canons pounded the airwaves, electrifying the sky. Streaks of lightning sought refuge on high points of the earth. Once the storm was above the granite outcrop, a lightning strike, which preceded a thunderclap by a microsecond, bore down on the rocks, igniting the tinder-dry grasses. The wind fanned the flames, encouraging them across the flat hill, heating the soil to precisely the correct temperature. The protective outer shells of the brown ivory seeds, safe in their resting place, were momentarily supercharged with the heat of the fire and the smoke effect, and in that moment one of the great miracles of life occurred. Enzymatic changes, deep within the recesses of the endocarp where the fertilised embryo rested, caused the seed to awaken from its hibernatory slumber. Not long thereafter, once the electrical storm had moved on to enrich and honour more mysterious secret gardens, soft penetrating rain fell. It came in waves of delicate drops, penetrating, moistening and softening the soil.

The seed absorbed the moisture, cherishing every molecule. Each fertile embryo, ready for its duty of replenishment, had slowly cracked. A single, pale rootlet searched downwards, and mono-stems thrust upwards.

After breaking through the surface of the soil, the stems surged, forging themselves into seedlings which, nurtured by the sun and the rain and protected by one another, grew into the small forest where the elephants now stood, teetering against the driving, gusting gale.

The to-and-fro motion of the trees, created by the onslaught of the wind, caused one of the trees in the lee of the blast to lean further in towards the other trees, lifting its flat root system off the surface of the granite outcrop. The tiny roots, which over the moons had tried so desperately to establish footholds in the shallow soil, were ripped from their moorings. The huge tree's branches acted like a vast umbrella or the wings of an enormous kite and the roots were torn from their anchorage. The tree lurched inwards. Like dominoes, the trees succumbed to the pressure of their neighbours. Their intertwined stems came swaying and crashing to the floor of the forest.

The elephants, seeking refuge from within, were struck by falling debris. Each animal was swept to the ground by the commotion of twisted branches and splintering stems. Panic erupted in the herd, with the adults attempting to protect their calves as well as to flee for their own safety.

The Matriarch, assisted by the sheer bulk of her form, quickly recovered from her fall while issuing a series of loud distress calls and *Let's go* rumbles. The rest of the herd moved awkwardly through the entanglement. There was a lull in the wind.

Standing on the outskirts of the devastation, the traumatised animals milled about in confusion. A fallen branch had severely torn one of the young bull's ears and two members of the herd were missing. The Matriarch initiated a fear trumpet followed by an infrasonic alarm call. She stood quite still and, with the exception of the odd creak and groan from the fallen trees, there was an ominous silence.

The Matriarch again called in a low, pleading pulsation. She extended her ears while leaning forward and facing the fallen forest. She lifted her front left foot, and held her trunk up in the shape of a question mark, appealing for an indication as to where the two missing members of her family were. The deepest most profound recesses of her instinctive mind were telling the Matriarch to move, and to move quickly.

And then there was a murmur, followed by a desperate, almost inaudible squeak, like the sound of a squashed bugle. The Matriarch called again, seeking some indication of the direction in which to begin her search. There was another yelp, although this time it was less audible.

Assisted by other members of the herd the elephants started doing what elephants do best – moving timber.

Working as a team, they shifted the mounds of criss-crossed fallen trees. By adapting their front footpads and strong front legs as levers, the adults were able to hold the branches down while breaking them. They moved them up and sideways with their trunks and tusks and lifted whole logs torn apart by the storm, throwing them recklessly to one side, the urgency quite evident in the manner of their work.

The calves too wished to help. Letaba and the others jostled for position, their tiny trunks busily picking up and moving branches where they could manage. Letaba was amazed at the golden-brown, intensely grained heartwood of the huge mature stems of the trees. But the calves' enthusiasm overcame them and Letaba nearly went for a permanent stay with Lord Rijhna when the roots of a huge stump almost fell on top of him. His mother, in her irritation, prodded and trumpeted at him to stay back. Every now and then the herd stood in silence, listening.

In due course they arrived at a desperate scene. Fearing the storm, Klaserie had sought refuge close to his mother and in her attempt to protect her son she had stumbled amongst the falling trees, crashing headlong towards her helpless calf. An entire tree had crashed onto his mother's side, instantly breaking her left femur. The multiple fracture rendered her leg useless. There were sharp splinters of bone protruding through the skin. She was in shocked confusion and could only produce a low rumble of sympathy and apology to her son. She was trapped where she lay, and his trunk was wedged under her.

The Matriarch assessed the situation. First things first. Klaserie was pulling as best as he could to recover his breathing. He stretched his trapped trunk, screaming pathetically. The tiny muscles, so desperately needed for the dexterity of his most valuable appendage, were torn apart in his trunk as he struggled.

One of the adult cows moved forward to assist the trapped and immobilised calf. She inserted her long, thin, tusks under the body of the fallen cow and, using the power of her head, neck and shoulders, pushed forwards and up, while lifting the dead weight of the stricken cow off Klaserie.

At full stretch when the weight of his mother's body was removed, Klaserie's trunk snapped loose and he fell backward, tumbling onto his bottom. And there he sat – tired, troubled, injured and utterly demoralised. He waggled his stretched and painful trunk, and then left it to dangle.

As the Matriarch moved in to offer comfort to the mournful young elephant calf, he stretched up to greet her and she saw for the first time that there was a kink in the middle of his trunk, only noticeable when it was at full stretch. It took

Klaserie nearly four moons to regain the full use of his trunk, and to adapt to its new shape – especially when he was dueling – but the injury would be visible for the rest of his life.

Klaserie's mother was in a much worse state. Some of the adults managed to lift her and she hobbled a few paces, but then fell again, favouring her right front leg. Tears rolled down her cheeks, her temporal gland wept and urine seeped continuously from her rear. Klaserie had to be coaxed away from his mother's side and encouraged to nurse from a surrogate aunt. For seven days the elephants disgorged water, feeding the incapacitated cow to the best of their ability, but within a week septicaemia had set in and a black cloud of blowflies kept a vigil over her wound. Maggots could be seen trying to cleanse the area where the bone protruded. Surrounding trees were dotted with vultures, patiently awaiting their turn. There was a putrid odour in the air.

The end drew near as the injured cow lost condition and eventually, at midnight on the ninth day, she succumbed to her injuries and passed away where she lay. The adult cows trumpeted their last rites and buried her body under a shroud of partially dried black Monkey Thorn branches and leaves. They compassionately drew Klaserie away and left.

As the little calf stumbled and wobbled along between the legs of the adults in the herd, Letaba was next to him with his trunk lying over his neck in love and support.

He was his cousin, and woe betide anyone who mocked him about his trunk. Klaserie would remember these gestures of sympathy shown by his cousin for his entire life. He was older and would look after him when they grew up, for, unknown to these elephant bull calves, their lives would unfold in a way least expected.

But for the moment, oh, how he missed his mother!

16

A transfer of authority

There was no fuss and bother at the inauguration of Mma-Thohoyandou. She was simply installed, respected and henceforth referred to as the African elephant goddess, the goddess of biodiversity, the daughter of *ubuntu*, the goddess of gender diversity and the custodian of all the elephants in Africa, both *Loxodonta africana* and *Loxodonta cyclotis*. Through the royal house of the Venda people and with the input of the wise rural counsellors and the shades, ancient beliefs and links to the area known as Thohoyandou were imparted to the newly appointed African elephant goddess.

At the inauguration ceremony, The *zwidzimu* (shades) spoke, and multiple elephant thoughts were transposed to Mma-Thohoyandou, giving her the guidance and leadership she required, informing her of an elephant bloodline.

There is an imposing image in the head and facial expression of an elephant. It gives the impression of being calm, at peace, and in equanimity with its surroundings. *So Mma-*

Thohoyandou, be like the elephant, as we the people should be like the elephant.

The head is very dignified and is not out of proportion with its body. *Retain the same proportionality in the way you live your life.*

The elephant, comparatively speaking, is a rather patient animal only roused if tested. *Emulate the elephant's generally considered approach to life.*

Elephants have powerful memories. *So try to remember what you have said, done and seen. It is easier to remember the truth, this becomes your reality.*

Notwithstanding the above, an elephant can become very angry and kill. *Temper your emotions, do not abuse your authority. Give wise and balanced council to all who seek your advice. You are in a unique position, with enormous responsibility.*

Take note of the topography of the area around this place in the Soutpansberg, this place of your inauguration. In places these mountains look like the head of the elephant with its great body below. And if you look carefully, there up high on that giant rock, is a painting of a vast red elephant. In front of it is a cairn, where respectful passersby leave small offerings – a stone, a bracelet, a coin or a button – a gift to the elephant.

The head gives balance to the body. When an elephant walks the head gives poise to the body. In this way the land itself has become a kind of terrestrial elephant, seen as a personification of the great beast itself. So the shades concluded. *There is a spiritual integrity amongst the Venda people and you Mma-Thohoyandou will respect, understand and honourably interpret all that has been revealed to you in your duties as the appointed custodian of all the elephants in Africa.*

Go in peace and with our blessing. Enrich the path you walk, give wise council and tread silently, just as the elephant does.

*Weave your knowledge, truth and advice to both man and the
elephant in this trying time here in Southern Africa. Live by
the principles of ubuntu – I am because you are.*

Mma-Thohoyandou will represent the future, to secure wild
areas for the children of both the elephants and humankind.

Mma-Thohoyandou's first task, albeit under some pressure,
was to bring about a moratorium on the culling of the
elephants in the Kruger National Park. This was forty-eight
moons after the birth of Mabitsi. Mma-Thohoyandou took
note of Mabitsi and his family, together with Limpopo's herd,
giving them special consideration and watching them closely.
She would monitor their progress and assess the predicament
of all the elephants in The Park. All matters relating to the
culling of elephants in The Park needed to be placed on review.
Working groups of conservationists, scientists, wildlife
managers and senior members of the tourism industry were
brought together to consider the elephants and the part they
play in biodiversity. Mma-Thohoyandou would be advising
and guiding both the elephants and people in their struggle
to come to terms with the growing population of elephants in
a closed ecosystem which fenced the elephants in, preventing
them from expanding their home range, their ancient
migratory routes. The elephants in South Africa now ranged
over only three per cent of the original land mass. Human
habitation had replaced elephant habitat, and the elephant
goddess needed to consider and advise all concerned.

But Mabitsi and his friends were bright young elephants,
cast from the die of some of the best genes in Africa. Mma-
Thohoyandou was slightly concerned about the orphan Klaserie,
but thought she would work on him a bit and help him, because
this was her job – and she knew he missed his mother.

Mma-Thohoyandou remains until today the custodian
of all the elephants in Africa. She is conscious of the

controversial nature of her calling, but she has learned quickly. Occasionally she produces an indaba rumble, calling the role players together, as she did on the twenty-first of October 2004, almost exactly one hundred-and-seventy moons after the birth of Mabitsi, a day most significant on the African elephant calendar. Mma-Thohoyandou was at Minister Van Schalkwyk's side when he published his proposed national policy on elephants in March 2007. She seems to be guiding both people and elephants in so many important matters.

And this is her job.

17

Mabitsi gets the message

5 years or 60 moons after Mabitsi's birth

The two herds retained and nurtured the memories of their experiences at the Hill of Hope.

Their wanderings took them to the central region of The Park and the four bull calves continued to bond, growing in stature and confidence.

It was approaching the sixtieth anniversary moon of Mabitsi's birth and, through quiet communication with the Matriarch, Mabitsi's mother had steered the herd to the Ntsumaneni Ravine south of the confluence of the Olifants and Letaba Rivers in the centre of The Park. This was Mabitsi's birthplace and his mother was committed to return there. She had to relate strategic historical information to her son, explaining to him how important the bloodline was.

Having arrived, the elephants rested above a glade of Lebombo ironwoods high on the brown granite cliffs

which kept watch over a pool in the river. Growing not far from this scene above the river bed stood an enormous solitary upside down tree, a baobab. The central branches immediately above the stem of the baobab had been cleverly cut away and removed a century earlier for a sinister purpose.

When The Park was established, a thousand moons prior to the birth of Mabitsi in 1905, the elephants would migrate through this convenient gorge. There were vast, largely uninhabited wilderness areas to the east of the Lebombo Mountain range, which stretched through and beyond the Limpopo River in the country of Mozambique.

In the dry winter months, pools of rain water would seep into the sandy soils and disappear, leaving the landscape generally inhospitable to game, and elephants in particular. The stream through the Ntsumaneni Gorge, though, produced a constant trickle of water which was the run-off from the mountains to the west, offering perennial relief.

The ivory poacher Briscoe, whose name to this day remains embossed in the stem of the baobab tree, had removed the tree's centre, cutting into its very soul. By doing so, he created a viewing platform high above the passage used by the elephants as they ventured west into the area which is today the Kruger National Park.

Through deep and sincere knowing rumbles – passed down the generations by the senior bulls and the Matriarchs – warnings were offered to the younger elephants. *Beware of this place! Acknowledge its significance. Never forget! Take care here!*

The herd had chosen this site for the birth of the young bull calf, Mabitsi, as he needed to know that many of his ancestors had fallen here to the guns of the hunters, but that it was largely due to their sacrifices that the Kruger National Park had become a place of safety and sanctuary. The area had been proclaimed as a protected area for all the animals and plants to flourish in. It was in acknowledgement of this that from time to time during their lives, the elephants would gather here, to stand quietly, to remember.

This high, central vantage point offered a special view of The Park. Instead of a place of death, it had become a sacred place for the elephants – a place of mourning had become the focus for hope.

Mabitsi wasn't quite sure of what to make of it all, so both he and Letaba tried unsuccessfully to push down one of the ironwood trees. They would try again later when nobody was watching.

A fully mature Martial Eagle was perched on one of the outer limbs of the baobab. His white and black speckled chest feathers camouflaged him against the lichen-covered limbs of the tree. He searched the river banks below, hoping to identify a flock of guineafowl or francolin that might approach the pools to drink.

Mabitsi's mother drew him closer to her with her trunk, while trying to instill in him the reverence of this most important location, and poked him quite firmly in the ribs while trying to encourage him to concentrate.

At that moment Mabitsi felt strange and strong emotions, and as he looked up at the baobab tree, vibrations surged through his body.

Although he didn't fully comprehend the infrasound messages, he did record them and would analyse them when he was older.

The sounds were delegating some form of authority being handed down to him, as it had been to so many other important elephants in the vast herds now scattered throughout The Park. The rumbles were as important in their recognition of The Park's history, as they were to respect its future. Just then

the eagle launched himself from the seclusion of the tree, diving towards the river bank.

Mabitsi took three steps forward to obtain a better view of the hole cutting through the mountain range. As he moved shock waves seemed to resonate out of the gorge. These tones resembled single rifle-shots, and they scared the young bull calf, causing him to back away. But there was no echo, only the feeling of the sound. Then he thought he heard the distant, combined trumpets and Let's-go rumbles of many elephants, though there was no sign of any below. The experience sent a series of shivers down Mabitsi's spine and front legs. What was the origin of these messages? Why were these noises passing through him? The young bull closed his eyes and at that moment a scene flashed through his brain.

Perched on a flat platform, high in the centre of the baobab, near to where he stood, sat a suntanned man with long black curly hair and a pointed nose. He held a rifle to his shoulder. Short intermittent bursts of fire seemed to flow from the end of the long steel barrels. There was no record of these shots being fired, only a shudder that vibrated through the young elephant's body.

He saw five large elephant bulls stagger and fall, one after another, as though bulldozed flat by a huge dung ball being rolled through the gorge by a giant beetle. The elephants' agony seemed to rise from where they fell and reverberate up the sides of the steep gorge and over its rocky lip. They were swept through and away from the place where Mabitsi stood. He swayed on his feet as these mysterious images passed by him and evaporated onto the soft breeze blowing behind him.

Bemused by the experience and having nearly fallen over, Mabitsi shuddered as he opened his eyes. He found himself standing alone. The rest of the herd had been advised to move away to allow him to live and experience these rare images, to absorb these elephant thoughts.

He turned and, with his ears open, he bugled loudly for his mother – and in celebration of the experience.

She walked over to where he stood and as she inserted her trunk into his mouth and onto his upper palate, Mabitsi felt the final encouraging message flow into his body. The only part that he fully understood from that very private gesture was, *When you are alone, be strong*. At that very moment he felt quite grown up and important.

He gazed up in awe at the torn left ear of his mother as a sticky liquid was exuded from his temporal gland, accompanied by a tear that rolled down his cheek.

Walking very close to one another, the two elephants rejoined the herd. The Matriarch looked westwards as the earth saluted the sun and, seeing another herd approaching, realised it was time to leave.

Mabitsi looked up at the baobab to see the Martial Eagle plucking the feathers from a plump guineafowl he had caught.

18

They all became big elephants

12 years or 144 moons after the birth of Mabitsi

Having made their way down the river bank, the amalgamated herd passed through a small damp glade. As they walked, Klaserie noticed a huge orb-web cast across a corner of the area between two trees. In the centre of the web was a silver female Marsh Spider. Her abdomen was cylindrical and slightly truncated towards the rear, patterned with red, green and gold. The young bull calf sidestepped the web and its owner. He rather liked this colourful creature.

Days and moons rolled into seasons and the young elephants developed and grew.

One warm spring morning following the first rains of a new season, a shower had cleansed the dusty sky: the atmosphere seemed sharp and crisp.

The three younger bull calves noticed that Klaserie was spending more time alone and on the periphery of the herd. His temporal-lobes were slightly swollen, and the adults trumpeted at him aggressively when he moved closer to the females. Three of the adult cows stormed at Klaserie with their heads held low, butting him roughly and trumpeting unkindly at one they had known all their lives. Klaserie, in his hundred-and-sixty-eighth moon and feeling alone, dejected and confused, kept some distance from the herd, feeling increasingly isolated and forlorn.

He was confused. Why didn't his older aunts like him anymore? Even his step-mother turned her back on him when he approached, waving her trunk dismissively in his direction. Within two moons, perhaps in sympathy with Klaserie, Mabitsi, Letaba and Limpopo felt their temporal glands swell. From an opening between their eyes and ears, a thin line of sticky liquid oozed and ran down their cheeks.

The three young bulls felt strange and intolerant. They were experiencing their first musth.

Within a few days, their mothers and the respective Matriarchs of the two herds seemed to show no further interest in their well-being. What was wrong with everyone?

The cousins decided to seek advice from Klaserie and moved out to where he browsed alone, using his kinked trunk.

He was delighted to see them and together the four young bull calves produced multiple male-to-male calls, played at mock charges and trunk-wrestled for days on end. There were times when the bouts became quite rough and Mabitsi often didn't like the way some of these games turned out. He felt a bit bruised at times and realised that he would have to toughen up – once Mabitsi had even pushed Klaserie up against a tree, piercing a hole in the top of his ear with one of his sharp tusks. The wound became quite inflamed and left a hole in his ear that would remain there for the rest of his life.

The young elephants slept apart from the security of the herd at this time. Mabitsi's mother had another calf, but he was not invited to share the happiness that was so evident amongst the rest of the herd at the birth of his half-sister.

One morning the four sub-adult bull calves woke early to find the rest of the herd had vanished: they had left during the night without a rumble. The four bulls called at length without hearing a reply. They stood alone, looking in the direction of the revealing scent the herd had left, shook their heads, then turned and walked away.

The bull calves didn't know that the Matriarchs, mothers and cows were acting out a theatrical wilderness tragedy that has been performed and choreographed through evolution and is tens of thousands of moons in the directing.

To avoid inbreeding amongst family members, ancient instincts override the love and devotion cows develop for their bull calves. Young cows invariably stay on in the herds, but bull calves are aggressively chased away to live solitary bachelor lives. As young bulls grow older and stronger their musth periods are extended during the seasons. They fight for breeding dominance and as their body mass increases, so do their chances of achieving successful mating rites.

Some bachelors associate themselves with larger dominant breeding bulls and become their askaris.

These four boys were on the move. Within days they began to appreciate their new-found freedom. They didn't always have to be quite so polite – they were no longer in the company of their sometimes boring family-members. This was fun! Or was it?

Letaba's temporal glands had begun to swell again. To his amazement, when he produced a series of musth rumbles one evening, as he'd heard other very important bulls do, they were almost immediately answered by two young cows in oestrus, not far from where he and his companions were resting. Letaba was off, like an elephant in a hurry. Mabitsi, Limpopo and Klaserie followed in quick succession. This was going to be interesting.

Letaba ambled onto the scene, cool as a wild cucumber. He rumbled his not very low-pitched musth rumble and then he heard Limpopo and Klaserie trumpet and roar.

From the corner of his vision, he saw a huge, grey mass bearing down on him. The ground shook. One look at this massive bull was enough for him. He instantly dried up his musth gland, stopped rumbling and, together with his three friends, fled the scene, pretending to all the onlookers that he had never come into musth at all. Far too dangerous a game to be playing quite yet, he thought. More practice was needed – and a lot more food and courage.

The young bulls matured. By the time they were a hundred-and-seventy moons old, they stood as tall as the first branches of a baobab tree, and as tall as the upper shoulders of a fully-grown giraffe bull.

Mabitsi's kept thinking that there seemed to be a great deal more atmospheric rumbling. The airwaves were overcrowded with communications between more and more elephant families. Where did they all come from? he wondered. What were they all doing here? What would they all eat?

The four bulls passed through an area where they had once all slept on their way through to the Hill of Hope all those moons ago. Mabitsi distinctly remembered seeing the vast forests of marula and knobthorn trees. There had also been those peculiar ground hornbills, with their strutting, arrogant gait. This time he saw only one group of these walking birds and they seemed to be searching for something. They seemed homeless, although they still said, *Eat more people! People! Eat more people! People!* in deep voices. There weren't that many trees left for them to perch in. Perhaps all these additional elephants had pushed the trees down.

The sub-adult bulls moved through this open parkland. It didn't have much appeal or shade where they could rest and fan themselves. And where would the vultures build their nests?

Late one afternoon, while dozing under a white syringa tree in some hilly terrain, the four bulls were jerked to attention by the strangest happening.

Below them was a young elephant with a large knob on the top of his trunk, running with his tail stretched straight out behind him. He was tearing across some open veld in apparent fear for his life, trumpeting and waving his trunk around his head and flanks.

While Knobnose had been browsing alone, a swarm of bees had exited the tree where he stood urinating. The swarm had set about stinging him on all the more sensitive areas of his body. A Pied Barbet with a thick bill and a red dot on the front of his head sat watching this performance from the seclusion of a Shepherd's Tree, mocking, *Heee! Heee! Heee!*

The young elephant had eventually left the swarm to defend their hive. As he saw the four cousins he walked over to greet them, still quite agitated by his ordeal. The boys were polite, and, knowing that five in a fight is always better than four, they invited Knobnose to join them.

The new arrival would often provoke a skirmish by rushing in trumpeting, ears fully exposed and with his trunk held high, but when the going got tough, he invariably fled the scene, leaving the quads to pacify the afflicted. He was an aggressive chap, trumpeting and bellowing at everything that moved. Klaserie thought he was ridiculous but was amused by his antics, so he let him stay. By the time Mabitsi himself was in his one hundred-and-seventieth moon the five young bulls had linked up as the askaris of an older, larger bull. They spent a few moons in his company and learned a few tricks. One morning the old bull became very smelly and they thought he was rude as he urinated everywhere; so they left.

The summer season had been quite rewarding as the rains had fallen in abundance, but the ninth and tenth moons of a season were always a time of pressure for the bachelor herds of young elephants. Competition for space and food continued to escalate with the increasing populations of elephants in The Park.

Elephants gathered in large numbers on the western boundary, slowly squeezing smaller, younger bachelor groups closer to the fences.

One evening, the five young bulls found themselves in trouble. A particularly unwelcoming breeding herd with a number of their cows in oestrus were in no mood to tolerate or entertain the affections of these novice suitors.

The Matriarch issued the attack rumble and a barrage of angry heads and trunks came thundering down on the boys. After making a brief stand, the boys turned and ran headlong towards and through the boundary fence of The Park. They found themselves in the private game park, Balule. This reserve too, was particularly overpopulated with elephants and the resident breeding herds and bulls made the five youngsters particularly unwelcome.

Led by Klaserie, they wandered westwards up the Olifants River, breaking out of Balule and into a stretch of ranchland owned by small-scale game farmers.

There was the sweet smell of lucern and the adjoining citrus orchards. It was an elephant feast. Seriously distracted by the activities of the five newcomers, the local farmers called in the services of the two Air Force helicopters in an attempt to drive the elephants back to where they came from. But there was nothing that would induce the five young bulls to return to that hostile environment.

The newcomers remained particularly antagonistic towards the process, trumpeting and bellowing and reaching out with their trunks at those wishing to pressure them into returning to Balule. The local nature conservation officer was summoned and had taken the judgement that one of the elephants was a problem, and so he was shot.

Knobnose's involvement in the death of one of the Malemela twins had led to his execution. The senior members of the community had followed Knobnose in the direction of The Park and had taken note of the large growth on top of his trunk. Knobnose was easily recognisable. When the matter had been reported to the authorities, some local farmers urged the authorities to destroy Mabitsi, Letaba, Limpopo and Klaserie at the same time.

A young journalist from the local weekly newspaper, *Kruger to Canyon*, phoned Rory Hensman.

'We'll take them,' Rory told Heidi Smith after he, Flippie Botha and senior groom, Jimmy Mwanje, had assessed the four remaining elephants on the ground.

Within twenty-four hours the required permits had been issued and veterinarian Douw Grobler's team was in the air.

19

Tembo settles in

13 years or 156 moons after the birth of Mabitsi

At EFAF's facilities near Mooketsi in the Limpopo Province, Tembo had been appointed Distinguished Director of Training, equal in status to Rory Hensman, Flippie Botha, Jimmy Mwanje and Frances Kampombe. Tembo was an ambassador for his species and his country, having met, and stored in his memory, the voices and smells of perhaps three thousand people since he came onto Tshukudu Game Reserve at the age of thirty-one moons.

He had been mentioned in regional as well as national newspaper articles, photographed and been included in glossy magazines, tabloids and tourism brochures and has displayed his talents before television cameras and on our screens both nationally and internationally. Tembo also had grand political aspirations, having acted as the ambassador for Dinokeng and met with the British and New Zealand prime ministers and the president of Brazil in February 2006.

He will also do just about anything for food. His continued training is fairly and squarely based on bribery and corruption. Tembo confirms that the bilateral ask-and-reward system of training works.

Tembo was a cull-orphan that arrived one day at Tshukudu Game Reserve into the care and protection of the Sussons family, when he was about thirty-one moons old. He became habituated to people and for years accompanied guests at Tshukudu on daily walks with the lions, cheetah, rhino, buffalo and other tame indigenous Lowveld game species.

In his teens Tembo studied for, and passed, his Masters degree in electrical engineering. There are few electrical installations that can confine him. He uses sticks and his tusks, as well as people, to test potentially electrified fences. He will gently and quietly push a person towards a fence to check if it's alive. If there is a reaction from a live wire he won't go near it.

After being traumatised by a larger, superior wild bull in musth in August 2003, Tembo broke through five double electrified gates and left Tshukudu for good. He established himself on the Olifants River Game Reserve where he is estimated to have caused over a million rands' worth of damage to wilderness camps. The owners quite quickly tired of Tembo's antics, and proposals were submitted to local nature conservation authorities to have Tembo euthanised.

Ian Sussons was devastated and hugely embarrassed by Tembo's wantonly destructive behaviour. In desperation, he phoned Rory Hensman and EFAF, a fledgling organisation with its headquarters on the Grootboom Conservancy near Mooketsi. Within three weeks they had been issued with a permit to capture, move and re-establish Tembo in Mooketsi, Limpopo Province.

There was great excitement in the EFAF camp in the preparation for Tembo's arrival. He was darted and tranquillised on a warm September morning by a veterinarian, Dr Peter Rogers. The team of elephant translocation experts loaded Tembo onto the waiting transfer truck. He was so large that it took considerable manoeuvring to fit him into the truck before he could be resuscitated.

Prior to administering the reversal drug, several blood, urine and dung samples were taken. From the secretions seeping from his temporal gland it was quite evident that Tembo was in musth, which would account to some degree for his behaviour.

After the administration of the reversal drug, Tembo rocked three times and then stood up, somewhat subdued by the short-term translocation tranquilliser. When he arrived at his holding boma there was a tumultuous welcome from an invited group of local citizens. It was the first time that an elephant had returned to the area, as a resident, for almost a hundred-and-twenty years. '*Ditlou di boile!*' they shouted. The elephant had indeed returned. When the back doors of the translocation truck opened the gentle giant lowered his back – with Ian's cautious encouragement – and walked out into his temporary enclosure, six large shipping containers which had been chained together. He was the most important new resident on zz2's Grootboom Conservancy.

Tembo walked straight from the truck and greeted an onlooker, David Beard, with a trunkshake. He immediately responded to offers of food.

But Tembo was not at all happy about being even temporarily confined. At night he would lie down and sleep but during the day, if he had half a chance and the grooms weren't watching, he would have his front legs up on top of one of the nearly three-metre high containers, trying to escape. It did not take him long to destroy the electric wiring that had been installed along the top of his enclosure. He simply took a branch from the daily browse provided, hooked it in behind the wire, and ripped the whole installation to pieces.

Nevertheless, with the daily training sessions from both Rory and his Zimbabwean grooms, Tembo was soon taught to sit down on all four knees, and within ten days they had a groom up on his back.

Six weeks after Tembo arrived at his new home, one container was moved aside and, with Frances on his back, Tembo nonchalantly strolled out into his two-hectare outer enclosure of trees, grass and shrubs. He grazed on the new spring-flush and after an hour he happily returned to his quarters.

Tembo simply revelled in all the care, love and attention.

zz2 are vegetable farmers, and aubergines or eggplants are established at the end of each row of tomatoes as an insect attractant. Tembo loved aubergines.

Visitors arrived daily, bearing gifts of oranges, apples, mangoes and bananas, and these people were Tembo's best friends. Everyone soon learned the 'Trunk up, Tembo' command. He allowed anyone up for a ride and especially loved having children on his broad back.

Tembo's human minders had given him the leadership and security he so richly deserved. There was no competition, and no musth, as this could now be suppressed with a vaccine – and has to be, when large elephants like Tembo are interacting daily with the general public.

It is only African elephants, trained like Tembo, that can confidently be re-introduced to areas where elephants have become extinct, without the often unaffordable expense of comprehensively electrifying a game-fenced area in an attempt to confine them. And even that didn't work for Tembo.

When newly certificated EFAF elephants are sent out to their destinations to conduct their interactive duties with members of the public, Tembo is often sent with them to help the new arrivals settle into their surroundings. He's often seen talking to and touching his charges, reassuring them with a special firm kindness and confidence, and offering them his own elephant thoughts of encouragement.

20

Tembo meets the boys

14½ years or 173 moons after the birth of Mabitsi

One hot afternoon, months later – and perhaps in acknowledgement of the need – it rained. The crescent moon had tipped the first of the season's rains onto the dry earth where the captures were to occur. In the late evening the earth turned to salute with a sunset this period in the lives of the four young elephants. The moon made infrequent appearances through the clouds, peeping in on the proceedings. The tranquillising dart contained the product M99 – Etorphine – and, depending on conditions, each animal would take from seven to twelve minutes to succumb. Within twenty minutes, each of the four elephants had been successfully darted near the Klaserie River, twenty-seven kilometres from Hoedspruit in Limpopo Province.

The first to slowly kneel and submit to the tranquillising drug was Mabitsi. It took only a few minutes for him to succumb, as he submissively and conveniently lay down one hundred metres from an access road.

Two of the remaining three cousins came to rest right next to the gravel roadway. (Klaserie, coincidently, seemed to want to be alone and was found lying some two hundred metres off the road near a dam wall. Perhaps he had been searching for his mother.)

Within forty minutes, the entire operation was complete. Dr Douw Grobler's team marked and measured each elephant, recording their height, girth, age (from their teeth) and footpad sizes. Their eyes were examined and a sterile eye ointment was applied. Dung and urine samples were taken for parasite evaluation.

The loading and transferring of the elephants from the recovery vehicle to the transport truck took another forty minutes. Once in the transportation containers, the animals were given the reversal injection directly into one of the large veins in the ear. Within ninety seconds the elephants came round from their anaesthesia and, after rocking twice, were up on their legs.

Each elephant had been administered with a mild seven-day assisting tranquilliser, Trilifon, to calm them during this time of trial.

Audible rumbles could be heard from within the containers.

The trucks were parked some four hundred metres from the tar road and were on quite deep sandy soil. As it began to drizzle the team realised that assistance would be required to pull the huge translocation vehicle through the sand towards the tar road, and a tractor was summoned.

Eventually they were on the road and arrived at the Grootboom Conservancy near Mooketsi at just past midnight. The crew were exhausted, but the elephants were calm.

The advice was to let the four young bulls settle in the truck and only to move them into their stables at dawn. The capture team caught no more than forty winks.

The earth rotated to greet the sun and announce a splendid day. A cool breeze blew in gently from the east. Tembo kept his distance, not wanting anything to do with the proceedings. He had been on his own with the full attention of the entire staff for almost a year, and this transfer of attention didn't suit him. His temporal glands exuded a slight, trickle of sticky liquid, attesting to his curiosity and excitement.

The first animal to exit the truck was Klaserie. There was quite clearly no time for him to miss his mother now. He meant business. Douw exclaimed, 'I'm absolutely amazed!' as Klaserie took three steps out of the truck, drank from a drinking bowl and moved down a four-metre, wide-poled security corridor directly into his stable. It was packed with freshly-cut branches from a huge red-leafed rock fig on the conservancy, and Klaserie immediately started feeding. He was guided into his stable, turned side-on to face his grooms, and picked up the nearest branch. 'I can't believe it!' said JJ, Douw's senior assistant.

Letaba was next, followed by Limpopo, who trumpeted loudly as he passed. Each animal moved into his stable without a fuss, and fed at once.

The elephants had been travelling two to a compartment in the truck. Limpopo had bullied Mabitsi and the team later found splinters off the end of Limpopo's tusk that had bashed against the side of the container.

Mabitsi was the last to leave the truck and enter his new world as a cull survivor. As he calmly walked down the passageway, he turned to look at the people welcoming him. He stopped near to where Lindie Hensman was photographing the proceedings, and rumbled. Then he moved on. 'He has a lovely temperament,' Lindie announced. 'He'll settle first. What a gentle chap.'

Mabitsi seemed to curtsey to the accolade as he stumbled on his next step. He entered his stable, turned, rumbled loudly and then started feeding on the branches of the fig tree.

Tembo was nowhere to be seen. He had retreated to the far end of the two-hectare paddock and refused to show the slightest interest in the newcomers.

The grooms were terribly excited. Most of them were from Zimbabwe, and everyone had been very down in the mouth waiting for the first group of elephants to join Tembo.

The first six to eight weeks of taming was the desensitisation period, phase one of the Hensman Taming and Training Procedure. Within the first thirty hours, Mabitsi had taken an orange out of Rory's hand, and the others followed shortly after.

But Klaserie still did a fair amount of trumpeting and charging at the stable doors in defiance of his confinement, and Letaba and Limpopo tried to lift the poles of their stable door with their tusks, producing disapproving groans and rumbles. Eventually, after a few days, all four elephants settled, with the grooms in twenty-four-hour attendance.

Tembo still showed no interest in the new arrivals. His trunk was out of joint. He point-blank refused to come into his stable at night, preferring to sleep outside next to a large tree with a groom at his side.

On the fifth day, two of the new arrivals started reversing up to the stable door and lifted one of their hind legs, allowing the grooms and Flippie Botha to touch and stroke the soles of their feet. But they did this only for a second and then turned to challenge the system.

'It's beginning to work,' announced Rory 'They're starting to see that we won't hurt them, so they'll trust us. It's a sign of concession.' That night, all four elephants lay down and slept for four hours.

Within a week, three of the elephants were confidently taking cubes from Rory, Flippie and the grooms throughout the day. While Flippie distracted Letaba with cubes, Rory was able to treat a pus-filled scratch on his head while also moving his hands over the animal's eyes. The elephant accepted these offers of friendship.

The grooms had, by the sixth day, managed to entice Tembo a little closer, to introduce him to the new elephants, the first of which was Mabitsi. Tembo stood back and only offered the tip of his trunk around the corner of Mabitsi's stable. The two elephants, knowing they were being filmed, rumbled, and then Tembo stood back: *That's quite enough for one day, thank you*, he rumbled.

The new elephants were moved from one stable to the next on a regular basis, and as they were moved, so Tembo gradually took more interest, and then there was an extraordinary interaction.

Just after eleven p.m. on the eighth night after their capture, all four new elephants, together with Tembo who was still bedding down outside at night, started a deep and intense elephant conversation. The building reverberated with a series of tones and rumbles, the likes of which Rory and Lindie had never heard. The dialogue continued for six or seven minutes and then the night went quiet. What were these elephant thoughts? Then the elephants slept.

The following morning Tembo was up bright and early, very interested in meeting all his new friends personally. Over the next two days his interest gained momentum and it wasn't long before Tembo was walking up and down the passageway, greeting each new face, talking to and reassuring them. Rory believes without any reservation that Tembo was speaking elephant words to these young bulls, *It's OK here guys. These people are my friends. They won't hurt you, so relax. Life is great here. They pamper you all day long with food and kindness.*

And so began a relationship that has grown and brought unity to a group of wild captured elephants.

These young bulls watch Tembo's every move. While many additional young elephants that were destined to be culled have entered the facilities at EFAF, not all of them could be saved. Four weeks after this historic occasion another four bulls escaped from The Park and had to be destroyed. EFAF at that stage simply did not have sufficient stables completed to accommodate them.

Tembo has grown in confidence in his new role as assistant trainer. He is the gentle giant he was referred to in the press. He conducts himself with dignity, compliance and the best of humour. Tembo has become, amongst other things, a teacher. And he loves his job. The thousands of comments written in the EFAF visitors' book are testaments to the sheer sense of wonderment that people of all ages have experienced when meeting Tembo, Mabitsi and the boys at the EFAF facilities in Limpopo and now elsewhere throughout South Africa.

At the time of publication, twenty-one elephants who would have otherwise been culled have passed through the EFAF training facilities.

Epilogue

*From 2500 years or 30 000 moons prior to Mabitsi's birth,
to the present time*

Where is /Kaggen?
We don't know,
but the elands do.
Have you not hunted and heard his cry,
when the elands suddenly start
and run to his call?
Where he is,
elands are, in droves, like cattle.

*Qing, translated by
Joseph Millard Orpen, 1874*

In the beginning of elephant time, after one hundred-and-twenty moons of drought and devastation, the rains had seen the wilderness that would become The Kruger National Park recover. The whole of the southern African summer-rainfall

region had had its underground aquifers replenished, and a carpet of green had been rolled out over the previously parched earth. Billions of seeds that had been lying in wait had germinated, bringing new hope and confidence back to the veld.

The man now known as Squirrel Hunter and his family who had so successfully performed the rain dance, could now pack-up their belongings and move north, home to the Kalahari.

Sixty moons previously, Squirrel Hunter's family had, as drought refugees, retreated south from the central Kalahari. Their ancestral home had been entirely depleted of food. They had settled in an area which stretched across the arid, northern hills to the west of the Phugwane River, where many huge baobab trees previously grew. This area too was dry, with only a few of its residents remaining. Once the rains came, most of the vast herds of plains game again migrated north. Regional species such as the gemsbok, springbok and ostrich had made their way back to their traditional grazing habitat.

The bushman watched at a distance, waiting for a sign.

Summer rains fell again, nurturing the soil and the grazing and, on a bright day sixteen moons after the baobab had germinated, the bushman family was on the move.

The family established their temporary home two days' walk north of Thohoyandou and the Mountains of Salt, at the confluence of the Limpopo and Shashi Rivers. They admired the shapes of elephants that seemed moulded amongst the granite rocks high above where they travelled. The terrain was flat at first and then became broken and undulating. The family settled with a sense of expectation in the weathered sandstone caves beneath the small cliffs. There were eerie secrets in this place known as Mapungubwe.

From a high, steep-sided platform lookout, Squirrel Hunter scanned the area to the north. To the side of the setting sun on the opposite bank of the Limpopo was the land known as Great Zimbabwe. Where the earth greeted the sun at dawn was the southern reach of his home, known as the Kalahari.

The San clan passed through a cutting in a sandstone embankment before reaching and climbing up the Mapungubwe platform. Along this ridge, Squirrel Hunter planted the twelve black baobab seeds he had collected near the Phugwane River. They are still growing there today.

Secure on their hilltop retreat, some members of the !Kung band waited, and the shamans in the band had a premonition.

One member of the band lay on his sickbed. He was lying under the shade of an enormous fever tree, curled up in agony in the foetal position. He was suffering from a sting inflicted by a parabutis scorpion he had trodden on. The earth rotated, placing the sun immediately overhead, and it bore down on the invalid. The air was clear and filled with the sounds of an environment bursting at the seams. A fish eagle announced from the top of the fever tree, *There's no fish here; there's no fish here*, while throwing his auburn head back to reveal his white neck and breast feathers.

The previous evening the band performed a healing dance. In this !Kung family, approximately half the men and one third of the women were shamans or medicine people. These were persons who, while in a trance, could interact with the supernatural world to bring about healing in a physical, psychological and spiritual sense to individuals in the band, as well as the band as a social and economic unit. This was the fourth time in the moon that the band had gathered together. On that night their dance had a specific purpose.

The women sat in a tight circle around the central fire, singing and clapping the rhythm of special songs which were said to possess /nom, a kind of festive energy and spiritual power. The mood was light and jovial, but gradually intensified as the vigour of the clapping and singing grew. Those who were able began to enter the trance; /nom was being activated. The fire at the centre of the dance offered the !Kung great power, and heated up the /nom, so healers danced as close to the fire as they could, in an effort to boil it. The flames of the fire leapt above the heads of the dancers, licking the night sky, cleansing the air. The smoke accompanying these yellow tongues was blue-grey and offered whiffs of tamboti.

Supernatural potency residing in their gebesi, the abdomen between the diaphragm and the waist, and especially in the liver and spleen, began to boil, to vaporise and to rise up into the dancers' spines. As the /nom reached a point at the base of the skull in a few of the dancers, it exploded.

Then the experience of kia began. The shaman had entered a world between life and death, betwixt the natural and the supernatural.

At this point the sick man rose from his litter. His heart appeared to stop as he feigned death, his thoughts were void of comprehension and he breathed with great difficulty. He began to see things; /nom things. His eyes cleared and he could see the people around him more distinctly. He was alive and he was healing.

Certain shamans were acknowledged to possess springbok medicine and others that of the locust; yet others, that of the elephant. The !Kung believed that sickness came to them from the great god in the form of tiny invisible arrows. During the dance, one particular shaman who had eland medicine had caused a great eland bull actually to appear to the healer beyond the light of the central fire, with the flames dancing around its head and dewlap.

A few remaining embers of the huge fire caused a thin column of smoke to rise into the blue sky. Assisted by warm updraughts of air, these eddies soared through the encampment. The smoke rolled and tucked, taking on the shape and form of an elephant. This elephant medicine gave strength to the scorpion victim, and he was healed.

The men and women stood together and urinated onto the desert sand. As they all reflected for a moment in relief, they felt and heard a series of sharp clicking sounds. The group concentrated for a moment and then, in recognition of the origin of these reports, they turned to one another with expressions charged with emotional wonderment and joy.

'It's the eland! They have arrived. They are moving north.'

The !Kung clapped their hands silently, and swiftly moved to check the wind direction. The wind was blowing from where the earth would salute the sun as it dipped over the horizon. When eland walk they produce a clicking sound from cartilage in and around their knee-caps. The sound is very distinctive, and with the wind in one's favour it can be heard from some distance away. The patient with the scorpion bite had recovered and the significance of the appearance of the eland, following the trance dance, had immediately become apparent.

The band speedily gathered their belongings together and prepared for the final leg of their journey, back across the muddy Limpopo River. They would head north behind the eland, back home to the Kalahari.

With one small baby secured on his mother's back and their possessions safe in bundles of antelope skin, the group stood and listened once again. This time they could feel the ground reverberate as the herd of eland approached.

Clouds of fine dust boiled into the atmosphere and the !Kung watched the animals approaching. The herd was enormous, spreading back to the low horizon, perhaps sent by the Tree of Life himself.

Lord Rijhna too, must have contributed to this process of replenishment, for there were elephants following the eland. The antelope stretched across the landscape in a broad fawn-coloured fan. The shape of the approaching herd narrowed as they sauntered in threes and fours through a gap in the weathered stone ridge just south of Mapungubwe and headed for the river below where the band sat watching, awestruck. The eland came to a controlled halt as they approached the southern bank of the mighty Limpopo, swollen from summer rains. The animals gathered and milled around waiting for leadership. Squirrel Hunter stood close to the girl to whom he would offer a tangy drink, lovingly prepared from seeds of the baobab and sweetened with a few drops of honey once they were home. They smiled at one another and marvelled at the sight of the eland. Good times lay ahead.

From the centre of the herd, a dark, almost black, eland bull, whose head and shoulders emerged above the other animals, pushed forward. His dewlap swayed rhythmically from his powerful neck, like a woven baobab carpet drying in the breeze. He lifted his proud head, flaunting his long, spiral horns. He pressed for an opening through the dusty, directionless throng, eventually coming to a standstill on the sandy banks of the Limpopo River. He stood gazing north for a moment. Abruptly he turned in the direction of the oncoming wind. Obligingly, the mass moved to follow him.

Some half a day's trot up-river, at a place where the rocks protruded above the water, the eland stopped. They mingled nervously amongst one another, anxious for the first of them to cross the river, in the compulsive need to keep moving north. Once again the black bull moved forward and trotted proudly across the stepping-stones in the water. Occasionally he lost his footing, but the confidence that he instilled in the remainder of the herd caused them to surge into the flowing water and clamber and bounce through the muddy torrent. The eland scrambled up the bank of the northern shore of the river, creating pathways in the form of narrow cuttings up its sides. Two calves were jostled and fell over, only to be swept away by the floodwaters. Africa's Nile crocodiles would assist in their demise.

The band of thirty-eight San clansmen watched from a distance. This vast walking pantry gave the hunters new hope and confidence in the future: no more squirrel meals. The eland is one of the largest and most beautiful of the southern African bovines; a male can weigh up to a thousand kilograms and a female seven hundred-and-fifty kilograms. The animals are pale fawn or tawny in colour, becoming lighter under their bellies with a large dewlap and a ridge of dark hair that runs along the top of their necks and back – both a browser and a grazer. It is also the most frequently depicted animal in southern African rock art. The eland was the creature that Kaggen, the mantis, created and loved. An old eland bull turns grey-blue to black as it ages, and has a majesty about him when he runs.

Bushman artists did not necessarily paint what they ate; if they had done, the most prominent subjects in their art would have been the berries, nuts and roots, collected by the women. Hyraxes, tortoises, partridges, lizards, squirrels and porcupines made up part of their daily diet, yet there remain few paintings incorporating veld food, birds or smaller animals.

The eland was, and remains, a significant feature in three of the bushmen's most basic rites of ritual: a boy's first kill, a girl's first menstruation, and marriage. In each of these the fat of the eland plays an important part.

The circle of events was now almost complete.

Squirrel Hunter's previous wife had passed away and was buried near their temporary southern home fifty-eight moons prior to the great deluge. Before leaving the banks of the Phugwane River her remains were carefully exhumed from the shallow grave. Her bones and skull were bundled securely for ritual reburial once they reached their desert home back in the Kalahari. One hundred and ten moons prior to her death, she had borne him a son. The young lad had, in his adolescent years, after watching and learning from his father, killed spring hares and guineafowl. These were followed by his bringing home a grey duiker. His father had proudly informed him why the duiker was so important.

As a skilled beginner, in his one-hundred-and-sixty-eighth moon or fourteenth human year, the boy was being prepared for his first kill of a large game animal. His father had chosen for him an eland bull. The boy would draw on all that he had been taught. His father secretly recorded the shape of the hoof print of the large black bull which showed such leadership in the herd they followed north on their return to the Kalahari. The right back hoofprint was ever so slightly splayed. This bull showed the class of leadership he wished his son to adopt. He also noticed a younger apprentice bull which stood close to the leader of the herd. Perhaps the younger bull was the great bull's offspring. He instinctively knew not to hunt the huge black bull; it carried the heritage of the eland and must be protected. But the lighter, smaller bull was a fine specimen and would yield enough fat for two people to carry.

The two hunters woke to prepare their bows and arrowheads. The previous moon, the boy had been shown how to cut and make the wooden bow from a raisin bush. A thin branch was cut and roughly shaped to taper gradually almost to a point at each end. The sinew from the hind legs of the grey duiker was stripped and twisted together. This string was attached to the bow with a simple slip knot and wound tightly several times round the basal end of the bow stave, to which a small leather bag made from the scrotum of a steenbok was attached. This prevented the string from slipping when it was hitched over the end. The bow was kept permanently strung.

The boy's father sat in front of his first-born and, as the world peeped at the sun over the horizon, he held out his open palm and said, 'My son, these arrows heads I made for you before you were born. I only once killed an ostrich and all these fragments of bone I split from the tibia of the black male bird.' While holding one short, sharp arrowhead he lifted his hand in front of the boy's face and said in a strong, melancholy voice, 'I once shot a squirrel with this piece during the great drought. That experience was most significant for me and seemed to signal a new beginning. Should we agree to call it In The Beginning?'

The boy nodded in agreement and then took the bone arrowhead from his father's hand and inserted it into the hollow of the reed shaft he held. The reed arrow was the length of his forearm, unfeathered and notched at one end to receive the bowstring.

The poison had been prepared by the boy with his father's guidance. He was shown how to find the beetle as well as the pupae of the insect, *Cladocera nigro ornata*, which forms the main ingredient in the arrowhead poison of the Kalahari !Kung. The beetle is small and reddish-brown and usually frequents certain Commiphora tree species, hatching its eggs on the branches. The grubs emerge and feed. When mature, they crawl into the sand, where they form cocoons and pupate. In both these stages they are used as poison, but for this purpose the cocoons had been gathered previously, and once dried in the sun, were kept. The previous day, the dried insect chrysalis had been removed from their secure cocoons and ground into a powder on a dish made from a tortoiseshell. The fine powder was mixed with juice obtained from the roots of a wild spiked cucumber, a rumputi. The roots were heated in ash and then knocked to the ground, and a few drops of the juice were squeezed onto the powder.

The boy chewed strips of fresh bark removed from the young branches of a buffalo thorn and spat the clear, bitter sticky substance over the poisonous gel. Once dabbed onto the arrowhead, it dried, becoming hard and brittle. Great care was taken not to allow poison onto the very tip of the bone arrowhead, thus preventing a fatal incident should it accidentally prick someone's finger. The entire procedure was done without any form of ceremonial ritual. The arrows and the small bow were safely placed in a quiver made from the dried bark, stripped from a quiver tree and secured over the boy's shoulder.

The boy and his father moved off into the desert-scrub; in search of the eland. They travelled for the rest of the day, searching for signs along the way. A yellow-throated sand grouse flew up from where they trod, announcing, *Watch where you walk, walk. Watch where you walk, walk.* The smiling hunters quickly consumed the two speckled eggs from the bird's nest. In its upward flight it complained, *Ha, ha, ha, ha!*

They collected a few rumputis along the way, which satisfied their thirst. As the light faded at the end of the long, hot day, the hunters called a halt to their search. Tracking became difficult and they needed to bed down for the night. Some dried meat was their evening meal and then they were asleep, huddled together in the open with their backs tucked against a sweet-thorn shrub; content, happy and proud to be in one another's company.

By mid-morning the following day, the hunters picked up the first signs of the eland herd, a half day's walk ahead. They ran silently together, breathing steadily.

With a light breeze blowing from the north against their chests, they eventually saw the heads of the adult eland above the low desert raisin bush shrub. Squirrel Hunter pointed, and there in the sand was the slightly splayed track of the big black bull. The younger bull would be close to him.

While crouching, the boy inserted an arrow into his taut bowstring.

'This is when you run like the wind, my son!'

The boy had collected tufts of long dry grass and wove them into a bundle with a few fronds cascading from the ball to resemble the rear of an ostrich. His father had brought with him seven long white ostrich tail feathers. They cut a branch from a knobthorn tree, having carefully selected one that had a node with a pointed round ball at one end. This resembled the long neck and head of the bird. By holding a stick above his head, with his outstretched arms, and the grass bundle secured to his buttocks, he bent his knees and took on the gait of a male ostrich. With his bow at his side, he approached the eland, while imitating the motions of the bird feeding, running and preening its feathers.

The animals at the rear of the herd looked up once, but quickly resumed grazing. Within striking distance of the herd, the boy scanned the mass of animals. He searched again, until his eyes came to rest on the large black senior bull. The lad marvelled at his size and magnificence and then glanced to his left. The younger bull, not that much shorter than the older animal, stood out amongst the others.

The boy hunter crouched behind a low thicket euclea and the ostrich lowered his neck and head. The boy pulled the short bowstring back until his hand touched his cheek, and the short, silent flight of the arrow found its mark in the centre of the right hindquarter of the younger eland bull. The animal jumped once, rearing up on his hind-legs and took off at high speed with the rest of the herd at his heels. A cloud of dust billowed out behind the fleeing herd.

Squirrel Hunter and his son followed at a slow jog. The eland were some way ahead and ran at a consistent gallop. The chase turned from minutes into hours, with the two !Kung hunters undeterred and consistent, Squirrel Hunter lingering some thousand paces behind his son. The boy ran and tracked without missing a step; his eyes focused on the spoor. He ran between the low desert-scrub, monitoring how the stride of the bull caused the eland to slow down and stumble.

Suddenly he was completely covered by a shadow; it was not the mottled shade that a tree would offer. He looked up and, facing him not fifteen paces from where he lingered, stood as large an elephant as he had ever seen.

All the words of wisdom instilled in him by his father and grandfather, over so many moons, were instantly replayed. By dropping to the ground and abandoning his bow and quiver, he momentarily became a monitor lizard. He hissed and slithered away through the sand, thrashing his right leg, mimicking the tail-beating of the reptile. The elephant stepped back, opened his ears, lifted his trunk and, with one trumpet burst, turned and walked away from this strange man-lizard. The old bull looked back only once, without altering his stride.

The boy's metamorphosis back into his human form occurred when the elephant was some way off. He smiled to himself, taller and broader in the shoulders. Squirrel Hunter drew near to his son, and with pride in their chests, they ran in silence, eventually seeing one animal lagging slightly behind the herd, and then they knew.

It took the two hunters another hour before they caught up with the stumbling bull, by which stage the earth was ready to salute the sun in the west. The poison had worked its way through the muscles and into the veins and arteries of the magnificent beast. The eland bull's tremendously heavy-barrelled hump hung towards the ground and he finally knelt in submission.

As they drew near, the boy placed his quiver at his feet and approached the dying beast. He too knelt before the dying eland and mimicked the bull, not in jest, but in salutation to the animal and a successful hunt. The boy had become a man. In acknowledgement of his courage and accuracy with the bow and arrow, Squirrel Hunter removed from his pouch two hand-sized, sharp, flat chips of black dolerite. 'These, my boy, were collected for exactly the purpose of both you and I skinning your first eland kill. These chips were carefully selected from slabs that had peeled off a large dolerite rock which resembled an old partially buried elephant bull, at a time which we have agreed should be referred to as In The Beginning. The rock lay next to a decaying baobab tree.'

While handing one skinning-stone knife to his son, the older man appeared to curtsey. 'This one is for you.' The boy's father held the other black skinning rock blade in his right hand and tutored the boy in the art of skinning such a large animal. From under his dewlap, down his belly, to a point under his tail, the man cut into and through the thick, warm skin without puncturing the outer stomach lining. Together they peeled back the skin, skilfully laying it next to the exposed pink and white body of the eland. The blades moved up the inside of the animal's legs, cutting around the fetlock above the hooves. The skin was parted below the neck, where it adjoined the head and was finally removed without any trace of flesh adhering to the inside of the hide.

There was great rejoicing on their return, laden with meat.

Squirrel Hunter needed to bury the precious remains of his first wife, who had passed away so tragically and so young. He had diligently carried her skeleton, exhumed from a shallow grave where they had lived to the north of the Phugwane River. He had carried her home, carefully wrapped in the skin of a young kudu cow.

One evening, while the band sat around their camp fire, eating and discussing the day's activities, Squirrel Hunter slipped alone into the night, carrying the kudu-skin coffin. With a stone spade and his hands, he prepared a knee-deep grave in the sandy soil, in an open area fifty paces from any tree. This would be out in the heat of the sun during the day. She used to love sitting in the sun; and this is where he would place the remains of his loyal wife. He sat quietly next to where she lay. Away in the distance a lion moaned. A pearl-spotted owl landed on the branch of a snot-apple tree near to where he crouched. The tiny bird turned his oval head around while securing his position, revealing two false-feathered eyes on the back of his head. He was a clever bird, always looking in every direction, and he announced, *We all weep, weep, weep, weep.*

The human mourner looked up and nodded his head in agreement. He rose, standing still for a moment and then he buried three baobab seeds a hand's depth beneath the soft earth. He patted the soil and then politely urinated over the sacred garden. He turned and moved off into the night towards the family gathering.

As he took his first step, he realised there was a herd of eleven elephants, standing in a semi-circle; watching him. They rumbled together as he moved. Squirrel Hunter knew that this was a sign and would give his second unborn

son special elephant potency, leading him on to become a shaman. Through the trance dance, he would take on the duties of the shaman – healing, killing the rain-bull to make rain and dictating the movement of game animals to ensure good hunting. Squirrel Hunter was completely content.

The rains passed on and as the waterholes in the Kalahari dried up, the desert family prepared to move into the eastern hills, where permanent water was readily available. The band set up home under their traditional dry-period, overhanging rock shelter. There was an artist's gallery above where they sat, with rock art depicting the thoughts and memoirs of their ancestors.

In a state of hypnosis during their ritual dances, the !Kung would record their memories and dreams as they decorated their dwellings with fascinating aspects of the natural world. Using their brushes of the firm hairs or miniature quills of a klipspringer, fastened to the end of a section of reed, they adorned the walls of their mountain refuge with a wish list. The rock canvas was a record of how the ostrich and the elephant fitted into their focus of life, giving them foresight and strength respectively. They recorded how the springbok and the giraffe galloped ahead of them during the hunt, and the eland so often became the centre of the artist's fantasy. They recorded why they revered the moon and worshipped Canopus as the Bushman Rice Star, the heavenly body that would ensure an abundant harvest of ant larvae.

The men and women danced, clapped and sang. With coloured ochre mixed with egg-white they adorned the inside of their granite shelters with the rock art that to this day still stuns the viewer.

It was early dawn and Squirrel Hunter, accompanied by his eland-hunting son, drew glowing sticks from the open fire and pointed the tips into the eastern sky. They moved the luminous embers up and down, depicting Sirius, willing the star to draw warmth from the sun on that cold winter's morning. The two men then covered themselves entirely in their karosses and lay down, huddled together.

On rising, the older !Kung bandsman informed his son that the ceremony was a warming incantation. 'The higher the star rises and the more brightly it twinkles, the closer the end of winter draws near, my son. And the sliver of the new moon is called a man, because of its slenderness. The full moon is round and is a woman.'

It was only then that the boy's father exclaimed,'New moon, come out: give us water. This will bring on the rain. !Khwa is our supernatural personage. Bring on the rain!'

The band was camped near a hot spring. With half an ostrich shell at hand, Squirrel Hunter extracted a handful of black, kidney-shaped beans from a pouch at his waist. It was made from the dried and salted scrotum of a kudu bull. He held these baobab seeds in his cupped hands, casting his mind back to the day he had gathered them, In The Beginning.

Sitting next to him was the girl that he knew would soon become his wife. Squirrel Hunter had prepared a fire an hour earlier. The flames subsided, leaving a pile of glowing embers. He piled the coals from the centre of the fire into a slight depression in the flat rock, which was soon heated to a scalding temperature. He flicked the coals to one side, blew out the remaining ash and swept the solid recessed oven clean with a grass brush. He emptied the brown baobab seeds into the hot rock bowl. As the beans were stirred, they began to darken. Steam rose out of the centre of the preparation. The beans were roasting.

The girl seemed slightly puzzled as Squirrel Hunter busied himself with his task. Finally, when the beans had turned shiny, tanned and pitch black, the grinder picked up a round, hand-sized river stone from near his left foot. He carefully ground the roasted beans into a fine black aromatic powder. Eventually he had made a pile which he scraped into the white eggshell receptacle with a dry leaf.

A Greater Honey-guide sat chirping, dancing and flapping its wings above the rock ledge where the couple sat. On closer inspection, the man discovered a vertical crack between two large slabs of mottled granite. At about the height of the tip of the outstretched trunk of an adult elephant bull was the home of a swarm of bees. The insects were busy darting back and forth, their wings glistening in the morning sunshine. A few of the bees were gathered at the edge of the hot water pool. The man had a woven rucksack strung over his shoulder. In the bag was a ball of dry elephant dung he had collected nine moons previously, in preparation for this occasion. He lit the dung ball and searched for a way up.

Above the high rocky outcrop grew a Large-leaved Rock Fig. The tree's roots seemed remote from the ground and reached down, like a climber's rope on the rock face. He planned to scale the rear of the rocky outcrop.

By holding firmly onto one of the dangling rock fig's roots, and with the dung ball pressed onto the end of a long section of reed, he lowered the smoking persuader to a level just below the beehive's entrance. As the sweet, dense smoke filtered into the hive, the partially subdued bees emerged in a confused swarm to investigate this invasion of their privacy. Slowly the smoke took effect, and the bees calmed. The climber then lowered himself down between two of the extended, light-green roots of the rock fig. The Greater Honey-guide stood by chatting, egging on the honey harvester and flaunting his light yellow chest. He was full of expectation, calling, *I'm the vic...torr, I'm the vic...torr, I'm the vic...torr.* The girl gazed at the man she admired, who stretched his arm deep into the crack in the rock. He held still, holding on like an acrobat. He coiled his foot around the roots, securing his leg in position. He seemed to hang there, motionless, before he removed his arm, retrieving a palm-sized segment of dark golden honeycomb. The one side of the comb was white, plump with high-protein bee grubs, and from the reverse side dripped sweet wild honey. The robber tossed the comb out and beyond from where he hung, onto the flat rock below, where it was quickly retrieved by the slender girl. The honey-guide was beside himself with agitation.

The girl broke off a section of the honeycomb and placed it in the forked limb of a star chestnut tree, which grew near. The bird flew off, bouncing from limb to limb, following the girl's every move. Once the comb was secure the girl retreated and the honey guide darted in to gorge himself with a well-deserved meal. This was a partnership nurtured in antiquity.

Squirrel Hunter had taken only what he needed, harvesting on a sustainable basis.

With a few stings to his upper body and one on his neck, he descended to ground level, excited at the idea that this moment, which had been sixteen moons in the planning, had arrived. He relished the emotion that the girl would show when she sipped the tasty beverage he was about to prepare. Boiling water from the rock pool was poured over the roasted baobab seed powder. The water quickly turned dark brown as the girl took over the task of mixing the beverage. The man picked up the honey comb. He placed it in his open hand and with his thumb extended and pointing over the steaming drink, he clenched his fist. The honey flowed down his thumb and into the hot drink. The air was bright and crisp and the way the honey sparkled in the sunlight pleased the girl. With enough honey to sweeten the drink, it had become the tasty beverage he knew would gain him the favour he desired with this young girl from his band. He smiled and relished the thought. He washed his hands in a stream below the hot-water pool. He lifted the warm half ostrich eggshell to his mouth and, by filtering the drink through his teeth, sipped the hot sweet liquid. He closed his eyes and dreamed of the sky – and more children to help him in his old age.

Squirrel Hunter was perched on his haunches, with the girl sitting flat on her aproned buttocks next to him, her legs stretched out in front of her. She lifted her chin and parted her lips. From the centre of her throat she produced a resonance more pure and earthy than anything he had heard. As she sang, the sound echoed softly away from the granite rock face and seemed to further calm the bees. Squirrel Hunter's moment of truth and expectation had arrived.

He turned on the pivot of his spine and handed the girl the steaming shell. She gazed up into his round, sun-baked face; she admired his broad feet with their toes spread in the shape of a fan. As she held the ostrich shell receptacle and sipped its sweet aromatic contents, her heart seemed to rise in her chest. She too filtered the baobab-seed drink through her teeth. The flavour washed over her tongue and seeped into the inner recesses of her mouth. She popped her cheeks, letting the sweet tangy fluid wash under her tongue, and then she swallowed. The drink flowed down her throat and warmed her stomach and at that moment a single crease appeared on each side of her coppery mouth. She closed her eyes and in a flash that surprised her, she felt a bolt of energy surge through her body. Her fingers seemed to tingle and her toes curled up at the end of her cracked, bare feet. What were these amazing sensations that made her head spin and her heart leap? And why was this honey-harvester now the complete focus of her attention?

She opened her eyes to find the man standing over her. Squirrel Hunter leaned forward and touched her chin and as this fawn-coloured bull pressed the warmth of his dewlap against her, the couple were swept away on the backs of a herd of wild eland calves. A Boulder Chat flew off, displaying a row of white dots under his black wings and on the tip of his tail feathers. He announced his approval of the union with a high-pitched, *Ho! Well done! Ho! Well done!*

The pair lay still and panted rhythmically, tired after their exertion. And then, entwined in a fusion of contentment, they slept.

In due course, after nine moons the family's number was increased by one. During her waiting, the honey-harvester's wife was treated with consideration by the older women. The short act of the birth itself was assisted by some of the women, who massaged the upright girl's back. The girl's aunt sliced the boy baby's umbilical cord with the sharp edge of a reed. The child was wiped off with a handful of fine-leaved grasses and herbs and laid on the kaross next to his mother.

As Squirrel Hunter entered the hut, the women – whose work was now complete – left the small family. Looking down, the boy's father proclaimed, 'My mother wishes to call her grandson Honey Badger. His second name is offered as Mantis and his surname is Son-of-Squirrel-Hunter. He will possess elephant potency and this will give him strength.'

The baby's father leaned forward and touched his son's nose and then his right shoulder, to confirm and marvel at the event. He was cementing a solid bond of love and caring. The boy grew. From a very young age he learned the wilderness skills so necessary to his future survival and the existence of the !Kung. The band continued to live in delicate harmony with their environment, in the way it had evolved over millions of moons. They ritualised nearly all they did, revering the heavens and blessing the animals with which they co-existed in their harsh, arid homeland. Days flowed into moons, which became seasons.

Births, hunts and deaths, as well as the ceremonial mystery of their trance dances, together with their rock art, remained their strength. And they marvelled at the strength of the elephants. The story of Squirrel Hunter during the devastating drought and the germination of the baobab In The Beginning, was told, performed and embroidered on. The tale was passed down through the generations, and the admiration which was fostered for the ancestral squirrel hunter has been brought through in the pool of knowledge of the !Kung people. In recent times the !Kung too have observed the population of elephants increase in the southern Kalahari. They have seen how these bulk feeders have impacted on the semi-arid forests. It was at a time when Mabitsi was quite young that the modern-day Squirrel Hunter's group mounted an expedition. They planned secretly to visit the huge baobab, which after germinating In The Beginning had surged ahead over so many moons, bearing upwards and establishing itself as a landmark on the veld near the Phugwane River, west of the northern, low, rolling hills in the Kruger National Park. They travelled along the ancient pathway, the track of the eland, the route of the elephant. They crossed the Limpopo River at its confluence with the Shashi at Mapungubwe. There they were told of the golden rhinoceros and the gold-leafed buffalo. In the gorge there were eland grazing on the flush of spring grass. They were mesmerised at seeing the twelve baobabs growing on a ridge of crumbling rocks to the south of a huge solitary steep-sided, sandstone plateau, which is Mapungwane. There was a solitary bull elephant drinking in No-Man's-Land where the Shashi flowed into the Limpopo. They passed through Thohoyandou at night and entered The Park down the Levubu River.

The group stopped in the northern region of The Park for a while to soak up the reassurance of the ancient settlement of Thulamela. They felt the presence of the golden necklace found on the queen's skeletal remains. There seemed to be an unspoken energy linked with Mapungubwe, the site where people lived some 18 000 moons ago.

As they walked South towards the Phugwane River, the group was shocked by the devastation caused to the trees by the elephants. So many knobthorn trees had been ring barked, their skeletal remains stark against the sky. Where would the vultures now build their nests? And there were so few Ground Hornbills. Where had they all gone? The elephants had pushed down their homes. They finally arrived at the base of the vast, spreading baobab tree on the banks of the river. Its grey, lumpy stem and branches seemed to resemble the skin and form of an old elephant bull. The group walked around the tree, marvelling at its strength. They chatted enthusiastically amongst one another, retelling the story.

Squirrel Hunter pointed to some encrusted mud rubbed onto a huge slab of black dolerite rock next to the tree. He wondered why the rock was there, why the tree seemed to have wrapped itself around the rock, incarcerating part of it within its fibrous polished grey stem. Part of the exposed rock resembled the hindquarters of an adult elephant bull. Perhaps this is why the animals rubbed against it, bonding with time expired. The story was true.

Evening was drawing near and at that very moment there was a series of deep, intense rumbles, causing the group to scramble for cover in the highest limbs of the tree. The members of the expedition hid amongst the canopy of branches and leaves as a herd of elephants passed under the tree; the largest female amongst them rumbled as she walked near the baobab. She had one tusk turned outwards and was accompanied by a smaller cow with a torn left ear, who had a young bull calf following her, holding on tightly to her tail. At times he appeared to have his eyes closed. 'What was he

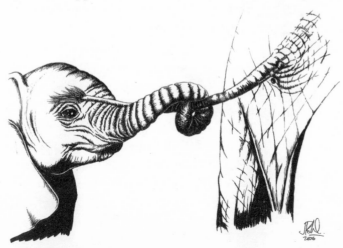

afraid of?' wondered Squirrel Hunter. A Giant Eagle Owl swooped silently into the tree. As it landed it turned its head right round and hooted at the people, asking, *Whoo, whoo, whoo are you? Whoo, whoo, whoo are you?*

As the elephants walked past, some of them lifted their heads and trumpeted at the tanned, lean figure high in the canopy of the baobab. Squirrel Hunter touched a leather pouch hanging from the loincloth at his waist with its stone skinning blade and a few crumbling bone arrowheads. There were also the powdery remains of some baobab seeds and the smell of honey. A crease of a smile appeared at his coppery mouth. He was utterly happy and content.

THE END

About the author

Together with the elephant's naturally gentle nature, the seeming ability to have a deep understanding of things around them, their incredible awareness of the state of individuals around them, their ability to open up chakras and make connections with people, combined with our natural interest in and fascination with elephants, makes this relationship a natural given (Thompson 2003, unpublished paper).

In 1954, my pioneering Cornish father and compliant Scottish mother left the tin-mining town of Rooiberg, north of Pretoria. They bought a small fruit farm tucked beneath the eastern escarpment near Tzaneen, in the Limpopo Province in South Africa.

From the age of five I played in the leafy mulch of the high-canopied rainforest surrounding our farm. I grew up a dyslexic

Howard Blight and Tembo

farm boy, who was given a Saturday sixpence and could buy a lucky packet for a penny. We had a pet vervet monkey, a mongoose, then a genet and a crow. My earliest childhood memories are of hunting experiences with my favourite friends, Bebédu and Mashadrulé, along the Mabitsi River, which has its source deep in the subtropical rain forest on the eastern escarpment.

I quite clearly remember plucking the snow-white breast feathers from a Tambourine Dove that Mashadrulé and I had trapped, prior to roasting it for a feast with marogo (wild blackjack spinach) and pap (stiff maize-meal porridge).

We swung on vines in the forest and climbed the great matumi trees that still stand on the banks of the Mabitsi and are estimated to be thousands of years old.

We regularly visited the Kruger National Park (KNP), where we had numerous close encounters with elephants. I remember never feeling afraid.

I completed my tertiary education at The Royal Agricultural College, Cirencester, in the United Kingdom in 1974. In 1991, I was appointed as the Wildlife Consultant to a Zimbabwean company, Touch Africa Safaris. In the same year I acquired a share in Giraffe Private Nature Reserve, now incorporated into the world-renowned Timbavati Nature Reserve. Giraffe Farm remains the sanctuary from where I draw most of my wildlife insights. This is where I first realised I had a special understanding for elephants, through an old bull we named Tatters.

People who have had close encounters and interactions with elephants will tell you that talking out loud to them works. They understand tone and intent. I continue to experience this time and again.

Explorer Mike Boon encountered this regularly on his solo canoe trip down the Zambezi River in 2003. When he camped out alone at night, breeding herds of elephants that passed within feet of where he lay would simply acknowledge him and move on as he offered them verbal encouragement.

In 2002 I rode Asian elephants through a tropical forest in Thailand and down a tributary of the Mekong River. Here too

I experienced a remarkable and sensational interaction with elephants.

On my return from Thailand, my good friend, Tony Somers-Cox, introduced me to the world-renowned elephant trainers, Rory Hensman and his wife, Lindie.

Rory, Lindie, Philé van Zyl and I joined forces and established the organisation Elephants For Africa Forever (EFAF) in August 2003. The aims and objects of EFAF are essentially to tame and train wild African elephants for numerous tasks and disciplines by using Rory's bilateral 'ask-and-reward' principle: ask an elephant to do something and then reward him with food. These elephants might otherwise be culled. This process has afforded me additional invaluable insights, at close quarters, with elephants both wild and tame. What my dealings with Rory and Lindie have given me is the understanding that elephants remain mysterious, largely unfathomed and fascinating.

I also visited Daphne Sheldrick in Kenya on two occasions, and have hosted her and been in the presence of her surrogate elephant partner, Eleanor, near Voi in Tsavo East, where I swam up close with a herd of wild orphans.

I can confidently claim that elephants do communicate with one another on a higher level than most other land-born mammals. Elephants can be categorised with dolphins and whales in this regard. They give and receive information through infrasound and their vommoran gland or Jacobson's organ. They have the ability to pass on information, and reveal an emotional state of mind to each other. They are caring towards one another and have a sense of family. Elephants truly experience a substantial, long-term sense of loss for their loved ones. We all know what good memories elephants have. But they also have a substantial sense of humour. Tembo definitely does – it's just that he can't laugh out loud like we do.

This book is a testament to much that we know and much we can only imagine, and so much we still need to learn from and about these magnificent gentle animals.

When elephants die

Pile upon pile of bleached bone and a foul
miasmic breath,
With now and again a mighty moan to break
On the hush of death –
Sluggish streams, and the silver beams of a
Silent moon on high –
God forfend I should meet my end in the place
Where the elephants die.

Cullem Gouldsbury, Ivory Valley

Seventy moons prior to the birth of Mabitsi, the last of Mafunyane's molars wore away and fell from his bottom jaw. He retired to the banks of the Shingwedzi River where he spent the final 24 moons of his life feeding primarily on reeds and grasses.

Unable to efficiently digest the required nutrients from this food source, particularly in the winter months, the magnificent bull slowly withered away, eventually lying down to die of malnutrition on the banks of the river. Mafunyane's body was discovered by Park rangers in 1982 and his tusks and skull were recovered and are mounted for posterity at the Letaba Camp in The Park, together with the other Magnificent Six.

An elephant's molar

Sick and old elephants often retreat in this fashion to the riverine forest and reed banks to eke out their final years.

Throughout the ages there has remained considerable speculation regarding the notion of elephant graveyards. One idea promotes the possibility that on rare occasions, when larger rivers flood and burst their banks, the bones of these fallen giants are gathered up and swept downstream. At a place on the river where it turns, the bones are deposited high on the banks where they lie strewn together, to be discovered later by other elephants and humans. Elephants have been recorded gently and sensitively picking up the bones of their fallen kin, in homage to lost friends or family members.

The history of
The Kruger National Park

See the timeline of the Kruger National Park, and some of the elephants in this story, at the beginning of the book.

The elephant herds must have looked on in confusion when in 1838 certain trek-boers, under the leadership of the voortrekker Louis Trichardt, were the first foreign settlers to traverse the countryside which is now the northern region of the Kruger National Park. This began a period which saw the devastation of nearly all the area's wildlife resources. Elephants were hunted and killed for their ivory almost to the point of extinction. These trekkers were at the time trying to find a route to the coast to establish trading ties with the Portuguese settlers in what is today the port city of Maputo in Mozambique (known then as Lorenço Marques).

The indigenous people had been living sustainably with the wildlife in the area for centuries and were naturally suspicious and antagonistic towards these tough, white, musket-brandishing newcomers. The Portuguese trader, Joâo Albasini, was in the area in the mid 1850s and assisted the Transvaal government of the day with advice regarding alternative routes through this so-called hostile territory.

Louis Trichardt was the first white explorer to pass through the area in 1838 and most of his family died of malaria soon after their arrival. By 1847 the Volksraad (the cabinet) prohibited any other parties from making similar attempts to reach the coast. But, by 1850, Louis' son, Karel Trichardt, did establish a route, although the exact course of such a passage was not accurately recorded.

Gold was discovered in the Lydenburg district in 1869, but the inhospitable nature of the lowveld – which remained a tsetse fly, malaria-infested, tribal war-torn region – naturally denied access to traders wishing to supply the mines from the East

Coast. By this time the depletion of the elephant herds was well under way, with very few elephants recorded seen in the area.

In 1875 the Hungarian-born entrepreneur, Alois Nelmapius, established the well-known wagon-road from the coast, directly to the Lydenburg gold-fields mentioned by Fitzpatrick in his book, *Jock of the Bushveld*. As a result of the Sekukune war in 1876, his native carriers abandoned their duties and fled into the hills, forcing him to relinquish his contract. Various small-time operators busied themselves in the transport business until the railroad was opened in the early 1890s. Elephants continued to be ruthlessly hunted.

The President of the Transvaal Republic, Paul Kruger, acknowledged the extent to which the wildlife resources had been decimated in the lowveld, coupled with the devastating effect of the rinderpest. This prompted the volksraad to pass an ordinance in 1894 enforcing an annual closed season on hunting in the area.

In 1898 the volksraad authorised President Kruger to issue a proclamation by which a tract of bushveld, lying between the Crocodile and Sabi Rivers in the then Eastern Transvaal, was set apart as a haven or refuge where wild animals might multiply in peace. This formed the foundation area of what is today referred to as the Kruger National Park. Then it was called the Sabi Reserve.

After the Second Boer War, which ended in 1902, the northern boundaries of the Sabi Reserve were extended northwards to the Olifants River. A further protected area was established from the Olifants to the Limpopo and named the Shingwedzi Reserve. It comprised some 800 000 hectares. At this time there were almost no elephants living in the area.

Over the next twenty-three years the Sabi Reserve's Warden, Major J. Stevenson-Hamilton, championed the cause of having the two reserves converted into one national park. An Act was passed by the Union Parliament in 1926 and the game sanctuary was preserved for all time as the possession of the South African People.

The Sabi and Shingwedzi Reserves amalgamated, and the Kruger National Park came into being.

It was fitting that its new appellation should include the name of President Kruger, who signed the charter by which the Sabi Reserve was created in 1898.

Stevenson-Hamilton had, on his appointment, instituted a strict anti-poaching programme throughout the area. The elephant population in the Sabi Reserve was negligible, a few individual animals that occasionally wandered in across the Lebombo mountains from the Portuguese territory to the east.

There is a ravine that cuts through the Lebombo Mountains, carved over centuries by the Ntsumaneni River. High above the bed of the river there is a dense, homogenous glade of Lebombo Ironwoods. The elephants would walk up the river from the Portuguese territory to occupy the area now referred to as Kruger. There remains to this day a large baobab tree growing above the gully where the river cuts through the mountains. The ivory poacher, Briscoe, had the centre of the tree cut out, leaving a level observation platform from where he would ambush and kill the migrating elephants. He carved his name into the tree; it's still visible.

This practice, too, was stopped by Stevenson-Hamilton's rangers.

In elephant terms, the declaration of the Sabi Reserve in 1898 and the anti-poaching programmes could be construed as a new beginning. Only at this time did the elephants first establish a nucleus population in a protected area. At the time of publishing this book, there are over 14 000 elephants in Kruger. It is speculated that, through deep, knowing rumbles, generations of elephants bring their calves to the river bank high above the Ntsumaneni Ravine, to impress upon them the significance of this sacred elephant place.

The Magnificent Seven

Adorning the walls of the Elephant Museum and Information Centre at Letaba Rest Camp in The Kruger National Park, are the skulls and tusks of six of the seven of the most magnificent and celebrated elephants bulls to have roamed The Park. These seven great tuskers were Mafunyane, Shingwedzi, Shawu, Ndlulamithi, Dzombo, Kambaku and João.

The bulls were collectively commemorated in a book, published in 1995 and illustrated by the renowned artist, Paul Bosman, with text by Anthony Hall-Marten. Dr 'Tol' Pienaar, at the time chief director of the National Parks Board of South Africa (now SANParks), had proposed the concept of celebrating the Magnificent Seven to – in some way – offset the largely negative attention which the elephant management and culling policies of The Park had received for so many years.

The result was a resounding success worldwide, in recognition of the outstanding contributions made by The Park's management towards the protection and conservation of our elephants in particular, and the biodiversity in general ('our' is collective: all the animals in The Park are understood to belong to the people of South Africa).

It is to some degree comforting that the burgeoning populations of elephants in most southern African countries are in sharp contrast to the predicament that elephant populations in most Central and East African countries find themselves.

The successful anti-poaching programme in The Park, which continues to ensure that most big tuskers die natural deaths, allows the free flow of their powerful genes into future generations of The Park's elephants.

The features of each bull that qualified them to be selected as one of the Magnificent Seven were their huge and particularly fine tusks, each with a mass in excess of forty-five kilograms (one hundred pounds).

All seven elephants were born in the mid-1920s and early 1930s and died within a few years of one another, aged between fifty and fifty-eight. There is speculation that the main characters in this book are related in one way or another to Mafunyane, who lived in the northern regions of The Park, and who died in 1983. He remains the most famous of The Magnificent Seven Bulls of Kruger.

Perhaps Mafunyane's genes do flow strongly in the blood of Mabitsi, Letaba and Klaserie. Tembo, too, is growing into a majestic example of an African bull elephant. At the time of writing, records show that there are at least twelve elephant bulls alive and roaming in The Park – with significantly longer than average tusks!

Two of these bulls stand out amongst the others. Duke lives in the Lower Sabi area of The Park and roams between there and the Crocodile River. Like Mafunyane, Duke's tusks reach to the ground and are chisel-shaped, so worn from pushing along in front of him as he walks. Each tusk is estimated at more than sixty kilograms (one hundred and forty three pounds). There continue to be numerous regular sightings of Duke made and reported on by visitors to The Park.

Mashagadzi is another magnificent bull and lives in the northern Shingwedzi area, the original home turf of Mafunyane. They are probably related. His tusks are estimated at over fifty kilograms each (one hundred and twelve pounds). He, too, is often sighted near a particular windmill in the area.

The Magnificent Seven certainly bear testimony to a significantly effective South African wildlife conservation policy, which continues to ensure the maintenance of a big-tusker gene pool for the future.

Elephant-culling in
The Kruger National Park

A farmer once said: 'If you fence off a large paddock and establish a herd of goats inside the enclosure, you only have to sit back and wait. The goats' numbers increase and eventually there will be no more grass and no more goats'.

The great dilemma facing the conservation authorities is the increasingly expanding populations of elephants negatively impacting on the vegetation. And when there is no more land onto which the growing numbers of elephants can be moved or be allowed to roam, what will happen?

The South African public both loves and respects elephants. Hennie Lotter, a professor of philosophy at the University of Johannesburg who also served as chairperson of The Ethics Society of South Africa, has publicly challenged the very broad base of the wildlife authorities across our country, to first thoroughly and comprehensively investigate all alternatives prior to taking any decision to cull our elephants.

Environmental issues relating to habitat need to be fully tested. Issues relating to contraception, bull elephant sterilisation and political alternatives need resolution in order to expand the home range of elephants into Mozambique and Southern Zimbabwe. The Peace Parks concept needs to be fully evaluated prior to any decision on culling.

Local journalists have a huge responsibility to inform the largely ignorant public accurately. The press needs to detach itself from the purely emotional traumas if and when a decision to cull elephants is taken. The public deserves a balanced interpretation of the facts, taking the effect on the biodiversity as a whole into account. The Kruger National Park and the various private satellite reserves to the west of its boundaries, comprise some 22 000 square kilometres – the size of Israel.

In 1967 it was recorded that 6586 elephants lived in Kruger. There had been a rapid increase in their population from earlier on in the century, and upper and lower limits were placed on the total elephant population. In that year, an annual culling programme was initiated as a means of stabilising the elephant population in The Park. Enormous ancillary infrastructure was established at Skukuza Camp in the south of The Park. State-of-the-art abattoirs were built. Helicopters, trucks and culling teams were employed and processing facilities were built to process and market the meat and skin.

The years when culling took place in The Park were tough years for the rangers and other conservationists. The ecologists and biologists had taken the decision to cull the elephants in order to maintain numbers between 6000 to 8000 animals. The people employed in the programme were split into two groups – those in the abattoir at Skukuza and those on the ground, directly involved in the culling operation. Culling took place for twelve months of the year.

The abattoir was designed to process a maximum of 800 elephants per annum. The same facility processed the carcasses from the buffalo cull. The ground crew was made up of 15 people. They drove the tractors and operated the winches and the cranes. On the day when an elephant cull was to occur, it was an early start.

For the purpose of the cull, The Park had been divided into four zones. In any particular year, the cull would only take place in any one pre-selected zone. Zone 1 was south of Sabi River. Zone 2 was between the Sabi and the Olifants Rivers. Between the Oliphants and the Shingwedzi was referred to as Zone 3 and north of the Shingwedzi was Zone 4.

During the period from 1967 until the cessation of culling in 1994, 16201 elephants were removed from Kruger. It has been calculated that the mean intrinsic rate of increase in the elephant population, between 1967 and 2000, was 7.5 per cent per year.

But culling as a management option raises ethical, social, economic and enormous emotional concerns. The culling of elephants between 1967 and 1994 may have maintained the population at between 7 000 and 8 500 animals, but was this the desired optimum range?

Park's management set upper limits on the populations based on the number of elephants per square kilometre. The Kruger Park's authorities tended to use conservative numbers relevant to other conservation areas, and a figure of 0.37 elephants per square kilometre was used as a norm to determine a sustainable population in The Park. So where did this figure come from?

The preferred method of culling elephants in the Kruger National Park was from the open door of a helicopter. A rifleman would be positioned above a pre-selected herd of twelve to fifteen animals.

In the earlier years of culling in The Park, the paralysis drug – Scoline was used. Scoline falls amongst the muscle group drugs, which first stops the locomotory muscles and then the diaphragm. With elephants, the heart keeps going until it runs out of oxygen, at which point the animal dies.

From the time the animals are darted with Scoline, until they are brain-shot on the ground, the entire herd would remain conscious, fully acknowledging what was happening around them.

In latter years, the shooting of the entire family unit was undertaken and the whole affair was over in two to three minutes. The helicopter, with the local parks ranger on board as marksman, would identify a separate group of a maximum of fifteen animals.

Once overhead, the rifleman would brain-shoot the matriarch first. This would anchor the remainder of the herd around her.

A military-calibre R1, 7.62 mm, semi-automatic rifle was used. Should a large bull be present in the herd at the time, he would be shot with a calibre .375 or .458 mm rifle.

The targeted herd needed to be near an access road. This enabled The Park staff to butcher and load the carcasses onto the recovery vehicles for quick delivery to the abattoir. The animals succumb in a group quite close to one another. The elephants are slaughtered in the field, with their guts left for the hyenas and scavengers.

These were very tough times for the conservationists who had spent their entire lives preserving and protecting animals and their habitat. To be involved in the killing of hundreds of elephants for mathematically calculated, population-reduction reasons, weighed heavily on their hearts and minds.

Elephants have always been acknowledged as being superior animals with greater powers of cognitive understanding; whether these superb animals should have their populations managed in this fashion, remains at the centre of a powerful debate. The culling of elephants in The Kruger National Park was discontinued in 1994, but is currently back in the news as a pressing issue.

At the time of writing, after three years of consultative debate and public interaction with the Department of Environmental Affairs and Tourism (DEAT), Minister Marthinus van Schalkwyk is revising legislation.

Elephant researchers

In 1957, Dr Vladimir Gavreau assembled a group of scientists to research the development of remote-controlled automatons and robotic devices. During this time one of the researchers started using vibrating platforms (infrasound) as an aid to vitality. He delighted in toning the body with these platforms of his own design. The effect invigorated the whole body for hours thereafter.

Dr Jonathan Goldman, a renowned practitioner in sound healing, observed, 'The intention is the energy behind the sound. We have all been at a party when someone comes up to you and says, 'Good to see you,' and you felt like this person has slimed you. So while the words (or the frequency) that were created were one thing, the energy was something else.'

Gavreau developed the formula frequency + intent = healing. In other words, the energy that someone (human or elephant) puts into the sound is as important as the sound being created.

After years of elephant communication research with infrasound in Amboseli Reserve in Kenya, Katy Payne and Joyce Poole were unsuccessful in compiling any comprehensive dictionary of elephant communications from their numerous recordings done on a daily basis. They concluded that elephants seem to communicate far more with emotions. Their remarkable research – and that of Anthony Hall-Martin, Jeffrey Moussaid Mason, Lyall Watson and Cynthia Mosse – proved beyond all reasonable doubt that elephants think, behave and react, in so many ways, just like the great apes, dolphins and humans. And on an emotional level the similarities are extraordinarily complex and similar.

Elephants speak to one another and they care for their young well beyond weaning. They purposefully teach their calves skills at a higher level than any species on earth, with the exception of the great apes, dolphins and humans. Like humans, their babies are born fragile and undergo years of training and guidance into sub-adulthood.

Dr Helene de Nyse, a veterinarian doing musth-suppressant vaccine research, from the veterinarian research institute at Onderstepoort near Pretoria, had been working with Tembo for a number of years. She visited Tembo at his new home ten days after his arrival at EFAF's Grootboom boma, spending seven days with him. When she left she wrote Rory a letter:

September 2003

TO WHOM IT MAY CONCERN

Tembo, a young elephant bull, arrived at Tshukudu as an orphan sixteen years ago. He became tame but was free-ranging, with another orphan female named Becky, and an older wild bull. He was never trained at Tshukudu and has been a problem animal, destroying fences and showing very aggressive behaviour towards rhinos. He broke out of the reserve in September and caused serious damage to the neighbouring lodges.

He was captured, trans-located and is now kept in a boma in regular contact with people and is being trained by Rory Hensman. Since this time he has shown no aggression and is far more relaxed than he was at Tshukudu.

I believe these behavioural changes indicate a reduced environmental stress, a positive response to training and an increased confidence in human company.

Dr Helene de Nyse
Wildlife Unit, Faculty of Veterinary Science,
Onderstepoort

This is the same Tembo.

Elephants do speak and think

Joyce Poole notes that female elephants use significantly more vocalisations than males. Of the approximately twenty-six vocalisations made by adult elephants nineteen are made by females, three are made by adults of both sexes and only four are used exclusively by males. An additional six are made by sub-adults. Of the twenty-two calls exclusive to females, nine are typically used to chorus with other family members, while thirteen are usually made by elephants calling on their own.

Elephant males call infrequently in the wild, relying on listening to local females.

On the other hand, groups of sub-adult elephant bulls in the EFAF taming and training facility do frequently practise chorus vocalisations, often at night while lying down. This is seen as a form of collective reassurance and comfort-seeking.

Rory Hensman quickly taught Tembo to talk. This is demonstrated on film with a hundred per cent success on-command.

Limitations may have been placed on elephant dexterity – other than their trunks – due to their bulk and design, but they have perfected communicating with their ears, heads, tusks, tails, legs and their huge grey bodies. But an elephant is most dependent on his trunk and the extent of its versatility is quite unique. Just sit and watch an elephant feeding along a riverbank.

The trunk of an African elephant is a uniquely sensitive organ, empowered with approximately 150 000 muscles and weighing up to 350 kilograms in an adult bull. The trunk has two finger-like, highly manipulative appendages at its tip. Due to its strength and flexibility, an elephant's trunk is considerably more versatile than the human hand. It's been said that if elephants had two trunks they might be able to knit! Elephants use their trunks to feed themselves and drink water. They bathe themselves with everything from water to mud, dust and sand – using their trunks. They pluck grass, twigs and branches to rub itchy places on their ears and bodies and they are able to remove frothy coagulations from their own or their calf's eyes, very delicately. Elephants have been observed using their trunks to pluck single thin grass stalks, using them as tools to prick open blocked temporal gland openings. They calm family members and, in combination with their tusks, attempt to lift injured or dying elephants and to examine their dead relatives' bones with the same appendage.

In combination with their Jacobson's organ, elephants use their trunks to smell danger, detect oestrus and to track musth males and – in the EFAF camp – to track and find poachers.

Certain trunk positions are used as flags to communicate instructions: by blowing through them, elephants produce trumpets, snorts and bellows.

Elephants eat almost anything that grows and use their trunks in specialised ways for obtaining various food sources. Clods of soil that adhere to tufts of grass are swept back and forth, or beaten

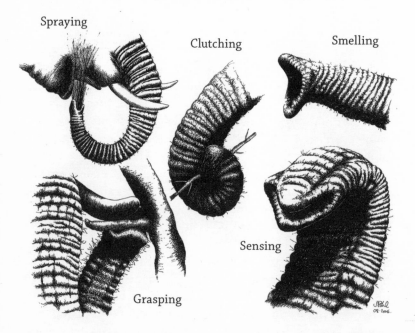

Spraying

Clutching

Smelling

Sensing

Grasping

against stumps, or onto the surface of water, to remove the heavy indigestible earth prior to ingestion. Branches are rolled around between their molars to help remove edible bark and, in combination with their trunks and tusks, to break branches, open wild melons and remove bark from trees, as well as completing dozens of other tasks. (In Tembo's case, the trunk is used to unlock electric gates, open doors to the food stores and gently break window panes right next to the latch, and open the window to devour the entire contents of the pantry by hoovering up every bottle of chilli and tinned preserve.) Feeding on thorny trees and shrubs often requires the dexterous use of the trunk, tusks, mouth and feet together. Elephants use branches as tools to scratch themselves and to desensitise electric wires while attempting to access new areas.

Baby elephants are born with only 35 per cent of their ultimate adult brain size. These youngsters learn by experience and need approximately seven to eight years of dependency and comprehension to more fully assimilate and equip themselves with the life skills required to take them into adulthood.

The temporal lobes of the cerebrum of an elephant (which in humans functions as the memory storage area) are very large and bulge out from the sides of their heads.

Intelligence is often difficult to measure, especially in a species whose senses are so different from our own.

Certainly elephants are intelligent by non-human standards and by watching their apparent concerns and interests, one cannot help but believe that they do experience emotions similar to our own and more than rudimentary conscious thought. We know for certain that Tembo does this.

Where in all this do we place elephants and the level at which they think?

Sue Savage-Rumbough has observed from her studies of language in chimpanzees that to qualify as a word, communicative signals must have the following attributes:

They must be arbitrary symbols that stand for some object, activity or relationship.

They must contain stored knowledge and be used intentionally to convey this knowledge.

Recipients must be able to decide and respond appropriately to the symbols.

Observations are made while the elephants participate in the taming-and-training programme at EFAF.

When out walking, Tembo often encounters a tree or branch that has fallen across his path. The command, 'Shift, Tembo. Move the log,' enlists an immediate, positive response. One can ride Tembo up to a tree and say, 'Push, Tembo,' and he'll push the tree over with his forehead. 'Pick the tree back up, Tembo,' and he curls his trunk around the stem and reinstates the tree to its previous position. Twelve-year-old Medwa is introduced to four people. Rory then says, 'Medwa, pick up the bucket and give it to Sera,' for example. The elephant does this with one hundred per cent accuracy, time and again.

The conscious evaluation and analysis required before initiating the attack rumble leaves one in no doubt that once the elephants have thought their predicament through and the word is given, more than instinct is involved. I experienced this on more than one occasion in Hwange National Park in Zimbabwe.

The questions remain, though: To what extent do elephants have the ability to plan and forecast their future? Do elephant families have the aptitude to collectively and cohesively scheme for their futures by helping to preserve their wilderness home? Desert elephants in Namibia seem to.

Elephants and their environment

Then again, why is it that elephants seem so extraordinarily and inconsiderately wasteful of their food resources? Elephants appear to utilise their browse material on the plains of Africa extremely inefficiently. Or are these thoughts human evaluations, incorrectly labelling natural elephant behaviour out of context? And what secrets are the balancing acts that elephants perform? Each mammalian species has evolved to utilise their particular area of grazing and browsing efficiently. The tiniest antelope, the dik dik, browses delicately on the very lowest branches above the forest floor. They are accompanied by the steenbok who utilise the finest grasses. The zebra, wildebeest, eland, waterbuck and buffalo are the heavy grazers who avail themselves of the bulk of the grazing. Kudu, eland, impala and bushbuck graze and browse simultaneously, while giraffe reach higher into the canopy of the forest.

Certain species like springbuck and gemsbok utilise the biomass in dryer, more arid areas, whereas setatunga and letchwe live in the swamps and marshes. The klipspringer prefers inaccessible rocky outcrops and has adapted its footwear accordingly.

But elephants invade all of these environments, utilising the whole of the vegetative biomass diversity. The sheer mass and strength of their bodies gives them access to each of these habitats in all weathers, through floods and drought.

Sensibly, what happened in Tsavo East from the middle to the end of the last century cannot be contemplated for Kruger.

Other areas suffered the same fate: Amboseli in Kenya has had its acacia forests substantially cleared by the elephants. It is generally accepted that elephants use less than five per cent of the utilisable mass from trees that they push over or kill by ring-barking. They seldom stand around and feed on the whole tree, often selecting a few choice twigs or bark fragments and then moving on. Elephants do often simply debark trees and by doing so kill huge knobthorns and marulas.

It is on record that in 1944 in the Satara area of the Kruger National Park there were on average forty-two trees above five metres tall per hectare. By the late 1980s there were fewer than two per hectare left. The elephants are responsible for this change of habitat. (But what did the area look like prior to the devastation of the elephant population a hundred and fifty years ago? Was it then an open plain with only scattered trees? Widespread opinion is that it was not.)

Proponents for maintaining the moratorium on the culling of elephants disagree with the evaluation that the savanna woodlands biodiversity of The Park can support an average of no more than 0.37 elephants per square kilometre of savanna woodland. Almost all the wildlife managers on the ground are claiming that there are just too many elephants in all our national, provincial and private reserves, where elephant populations have expended so tremendously in recent years, and biodiversity is being so negatively affected. There are more than three elephants born in Kruger each day.

Elephants have endured: they are the ultimate Keepers of the Kingdom, the top of the savanna woodland food chain. They live on as the supreme survivors. Are they able to intellectualise the process whereby they can control or reduce their own population growth, with the possibility of seeing it crash, as happened in Tsavo East in 1972? To what extent was this a natural process? Can the Kruger National Park and other reserves afford the consequences of such dynamic changes to the savanna woodland – and the possible negative effect on the number of paying tourists?

Wilderness sanctuaries such as Kruger are artificial in every respect. The area is fenced. Roads, dams and waterholes have been created away from the rivers and every year millions of visitors are drawn to The Park to observe the wonderment of nature on the African savanna.

People come to marvel at the full spectrum of species diversity, and as close to a balanced wilderness as The Parks authorities can maintain. The ongoing challenge in the management of The Park is to facilitate this biodiversity sensibly and sensitively.

Mice and elephants

There are ancient claims that elephants are afraid of mice. These assertions are found in children's story books, in mythology, in proverbs and in fables across cultures. Are they false?

Mice and other small scurrying rodents can and do kill elephants, and with repeated swiftness. And elephants do fear mice under certain circumstances, becoming quite agitated at their presence.

We accept that elephants are of the most fearless animals in the world. Their great strength and courage is often pitted against lions, rhinos and tigers. They will defend their young against all odds, which so often leaves them vulnerable to the hunters' guns. (It's a common misconception that elephants have poor eyesight. One of the EFAF elephants, Klaserie, became quite agitated at a rat running across a beam four metres above him in his stable. He raised his head and swirled around to meet his aggressor. As he lifted his trunk he trumpeted at the little creature that scurried away into a crack in the wall. Klaserie remained quite vigilant for some time and kept looking up at the ceiling, clearly expecting the furry monster to reappear at any moment.)

In 1993 there was a recorded outbreak of encephalomyocarditis; known as the EMC virus infection in free-ranging elephants in the Kruger National Park. This infectious disease marked the onslaught and subsequent death of thirty-two elephants in January of 1994, gradually declining to a pre-outbreak level in September. Sporadic losses continued until November. Altogether, sixty-four elephants died, of which fifty-three were adult bulls. There is the skull of one of these victims at a camp on Giraffe Farm in the Timbivati Nature Reserve.

Records reveal sporadic unexplained deaths in widely scattered areas of The Park since 1987, with as many as forty-eight elephants having died prior to the 1993/94 outbreak.

Carcasses were examined and lesions of cardiac failure (heart attack) suggested that the EMC virus, which was isolated from the heart muscle of three fresh carcasses, was responsible for the untimely deaths of the elephants.

Ongoing studies of myomorph rodents showed a striking temporal correlation between the occurrence of a population explosion of the rodents – and a surge in the prevalence of the antibody to the EMC virus in the rodents – and the occurrence of the outbreak of the disease in elephants.

So how can these rats or mice kill elephants?

During the population explosion of the rodents, the male of the species embarks on territorial urinary markings on tufts of grass in the areas near their nests. The urine harbours the EMC virus and, as elephants feed on contaminated tufts of these grasses, they ingest larger-than-normal quantities of the virus. Their bodies are unable to cope with higher doses of the virus and lesions develop on their hearts, causing some of the elephants to have heart attacks and die. (A rodent explosion, of course, has an upside to it. Barn owls have been recorded with as many as twelve owlets of various ages during times of plentiful mice. In times of abundance, the owls just keep laying and hatching and rearing more chicks.) Mice do kill elephants: elephants are afraid of mice. And rightly so.

Lord Ganesh, the mythological Hindu god of knowledge, the elephant god and the remover of obstacles, is the older son of Lord Shiva. Lord Ganesh is also called Vinayak. He has four hands and the head of an elephant, as well as a big belly. And as his vehicle, he has a tiny mouse. Hindu mythology continues to respect the unique combination of Ganesh's elephantine head and scurrying-mouse vehicle: he represents tremendous wisdom, intelligence and presence of mind.

Acknowledgements

Thanks must go to:

The many authors and publishers from whom I have drawn the inspiration to publish this book. To Richard Harland (author of *African Epic*, *Ndlovu* and *The Hunting Imperative*) who has written so extensively on elephants, and his wife, Bergita, for their encouragement and advice. Those whose writing has contributed more significantly are Katy Payne, Cynthia Mosse and Joyce Poole. There have been hundreds of books written about these noble, gentle beasts. Perhaps this book should give acknowledgement to the elephants' patience and trust.

Di, Wynand and Maria for the hours of typing and spell-checking of my hand-written manuscript.

Professor Hennie Lotter, for his extraordinary understanding of the plight of the elephants and his balanced view of their future. He has taken on so much.

Mike Amm, for his invaluable contribution towards the correct identification and naming of so many of the trees mentioned in the story.

Lyall Watson, a naturalist of extraordinary proportions, who workshopped this manuscript with me and whose experiences remain an inspiration to millions around the world.

The senior management at SANParks, for their careful, considerate and inclusive approach at the Elephant Indaba held in October 2004. I have no doubt that the appropriate answers will be forthcoming.

Archbishop Desmond Tutu, for his encouragement in regard to the concept of the folklore goddess Mma Thohoyandou.

Rory and Lindie Hensman, for their friendship and for allowing me the privilege of gaining some very close, firsthand knowledge of how these truly remarkable animals think, talk, and develop such impressive trust in their handlers during their wild-to-tame-and-trained transition.

All those people involved at zz2, who have assisted in turning EFAF from an idea into the staggering way in which it has enriched our lives. To Philé and Tommie van Zyl, I see how the elephants have affected the lives of all of us.

And finally to the elephants: Tembo, Mabitsi, Letaba, Limpopo, Klaserie, Tswale, Selati, Modjadji and Kidiborn, and others that will pass through the programme at EFAF. They will become the ambassadors for the kind of country that they so richly deserve. These young elephants will show us how to guide the blind who will not see, the deaf who will not hear, and the mute who will not speak on their behalf.

May the wilderness be the recipient of our collective efforts, evaluations and understanding.

Howard Blight, Phophoroga

Select bibliography

Books

Boone, Mike. *The African Way*. 1996.

Bosman, Paul, and Hall-Martin, Anthony. *The Magnificent Seven*. 1998.

Douglas-Hamilton, Iain, and Douglas-Hamilton, Oria. *Battle for the Elephants*. 1992.

Du Toit, Johan T., Rogers, Kevin H., and Biggs, Harry C. *The Kruger Experience*. 2005.

Hall-Martin, Anthony. *A Day in the Life of an African Elephant*. 1993.

Livingstone, D., *Last Journal*. London: John Murray. 1874, p. 315.

Moss, Cynthia. *Elephant Memories*. 1998.

Moussaieff Masson, Jeffrey. *When Elephants Weep*. 1996.

Mutwa, Credo. *My People*. 1971.

Newman, Kenneth. *Newman's Birds of Southern Africa*. 1998.

Palgrave, Keith C. *Trees of Southern Africa*. 1977

Payne, Katy. *Silent Thunder: In the Presence of Elephants*. 1998.

Poole, Joyce. *Coming of Age with Elephants*. 1996.

Rossing, Thomas, D. *The Science of Sound*. 2002.

Sheldrick, Daphne. *The Orphans of Tsavo*. 1966.

Stevenson-Hamilton, Lieutenant-Colonel J. *South African Eden*. 1937.

Venter, Fanie and Venter, July-Ann. *Making the Most of Indigenous Trees*. 1996.

Watson, Lyall. *Jacobson's Organ*. 2002.

Yates, C. A. *The Kruger National Park*. 1935.

Journals

Grobler, D.G., Raath, J.P., Braack, L.E.O., Keet, D.F., Gerdes, G.H., Barnard, B.J.H., Krick, N.P.J., Jardine, J., and Swanepoel, R. 1995. 'An outbreak of encephalomyocarditis-virus infection in free-ranging African elephants in the Kruger National Park'. *Onderstepoort Journal of Veterinary Research*, 62: 97–108.

Dave Cummings. Elephant Indaba held in 2005 at the Kruger National Park.

Film

Hensman, Rory, and Hensman, Lindie. Film footage captured between 1990 and 2003.

Trevor, Simon. H. C. Blight captured and recorded on film in 1987.

Glossary

African Wattle tree: *Peltophorum africanum*
alarm call: elephant warning sound or signal
amniotic sac: bag in which the foetus grows and is fed
Ana tree: *Faidherbia albida*
askari: young elephant bulls who join up with older respected bulls and/or an East African soldier

bellow: the loud, deep sound made by elephants and other large animals
biodiversity: the variety of fauna and flora in a particular habitat
Black Monkey Thorn tree: *Acacia burkei*
boer: literal term for South African farmer; colloquial term for Afrikaner
boma: an enclosure, often of thorn bush, to protect a camp or animals
Broad Pod Albizia tree: *Albizia forbesii*
Brown Ivory tree: *Berchemia discolor*
Bubbling Kassina Frog: *Kassina senegalensis*
Buffalo Thorn tree: *Ziziphus mucronata*
bugling: trumpet-like sound often emitted by elephants
Bushveld Rain Frog: *Breviceps adsperus*
bushveld shrub: woodland; thicket

Canopus: the second brightest star in the southern hemisphere skies, at 52 degrees 41 minutes south
Cape Thatching Reed: *Chondropetalum tectorum*
Caterpillar-pod Shrub: *Ormocarpum trichocarpum*
Commiphora tree: indigenous tree family on the African savanna
Coral tree: *Erythrina caffra*
Cyclotis: African Forest Elephant, slightly smaller in stature than the Savanna elephant. Full name *Loxodonta cyclotis*.

Date Palm: *Phoenix reclinata*
desensitisation period: time period to help young captive elephants to settle into their new surroundings
Dik-dik: small antelope found on the dry savanna of central Africa
Dik-kop: plover-like bird with large yellow eyes and long yellowish legs
donga: a ditch or gulley caused by erosion

EFAF: Elephants for Africa Forever, the company licensed to train wild African elephants as an alternative to their being culled
endosperm: with the embryo of a seed; contains reserve substances
exhume: to dig up an object or body

faction: a speculative mix of fact and fiction
Fever Tree: *Acacia xanthophloea*
Flame Creeper: *Combretum microphyllum*
flemering: a noise made by a bull elephant in musth
Foam Nest Frogs: *Chiromantis xerampelina*. They lay their eggs in trees overhanging water holes.
forfend: abstain from providing

gebesi: stomach
Gemsbuck: large dry-area antelope with long straight horns
gozie: African tribal leader or elder in the context of rural Africa

Hill of Hope: factitious destination; site of water reserves
Honeyguide: small, drab bird feeding chiefly on honey and bee grubs

indaba: meeting or gathering, usually to discuss a serious topic
infrasound: low vibrations (10–35 hertz) that travel through the air. The dominant communication method of elephants.

Jackal-berry tree: *Diospyros Mespiliformis*

Jacobson's organ: vommoran gland, seen as two small holes on the upper inside palate in the mouth of the elephant; used to give and receive information

Kaggen, the Mantis: a mythical creature in bushman folklore
kaross: a rug or blanket of animals skins
kia: the spiritual hallucinogenic state in bushman dance culture
Klipspringer: small antelope confined to rocky outcrops
Knobthorn: *Acacia nigrescens*

laager: a circle formed by wagons for protection
Large-leafed Rock Fig: *Ficus abutilifolia*
last rites: final solemn rituals or religious ceremony
Leadwood: *Combretum imberbe*
Letchwe: board-hoofed swamp antelope
litter: a stretcher
Lord Rijhna (pronounced 'Ridge-nah'): the cumulus god of Eastern folklore who speaks on behalf of both people and elephants
lucerne: alfafa; high-protein broad-leaved legume
Lebombo Ironwood: *Androstachys johnsonii*

machete: broad, heavy knife used as a tool or a weapon
Magic Guarri shrub: *Euclea divinorum*
Marula tree: *Sclerocearya birrea* subspecies *caffra*
Matumi tree: *Breonadia salicina*
Meerkat: mongoose
mono-stem: single growth point on a plant
Monkey-orange fruit: *Strychnos spinosa*
monster bull: a huge, frightening, fully grown male elephant
moons: lunar measurement; one moon signifies a single month
Mopane tree: *Colophospermum mopane*
Mottled Shovel-nosed Frog: *Hemisus marmoratus*
Musth: increased levels of testosterone
mutingati: biodiversity

nictitating membrane: a retractable membrane that protects the eye

/nom: an altered state of consciousness which occurs in bushman shape-shifting dance

Nyandubos: *Guibortia conjugata*, a forest of false Mopane trees

oestrus: recurring period of sexual receptivity and fertility in many female mammals ('on heat')

opium: sedative; narcotic made from poppy seeds

Ornate Frog: *Hildebrandtia ornata*

puff adder: a thick-bodied poisonous snake

Raisin Bush: *Grewia flava*

Red-leaved Rock Fig: *Ficus ingens*

Red-legged Kassina Frog: *Kassina maculata*

resonance: resounding, echoing vibration

rumble: a deep, heavy, continuous roar emitted by elephants, like thunder

Riverbush-willow tree: *Combretum erythrophyllum*

riverine: of the river

San: bushman

sangoma: traditional healer or diviner

Sausage Tree: *Kigelia africana*

Scented Thorn: *Acacia nilotica* subsp. *kraussiananilotica*

Scoline: anaesthetic drug used to dart and capture wild animals

septicaemia: blood poisoning

Setatunga: a broad-hoofed antelope found in wetland areas

shaman: a person who is able to communicate with the spirit world

Shaving Brush Combretum: *Combretum mossabicense*

Shepherd Tree: *Boscia albitrunca*

Sickle Bush: *Dichrostachys cinerea* subsp. *africana*

Snoring Puddle Frog: *Phrynobatrachus natalensis*

Springbuck: antelope
Star Chestnut tree: *Sterculia rogersii*
Sycamore Fig: *Ficus sycomorus* subsp. *sycomorus*

Tamboti: Spirostachys africana
temporal glands: found on the temple of an elephant's head
The Park: The Kruger National Park
Thicket uclea: *Undulata*
Three-hooked Thorn: *Acacia senegal*
tindlopfu: elephant
Tree Wisteria: *Bolusanthus speciosus*
trek: a long hard walk or journey lasting a few days or weeks
trumpet: loud sound made by an elephant as announcement

ubuntu: the African idea of common humanity, often explained by the saying, 'I am because you are'
ululate: Mournful, high-pitched wailing, usually made by African women, to show their grief or excitement
Ulumbyne: a monitor lizard
urinate: to discharge urine

veld: an area of open grassland
vibrations: quivering motion; tremulousness
vigil: keeping watch, especially at night
vlei: marshland or meadow
voortrekker: early Afrikaner pioneer

Weeping Boer Bean: *Schotia brachypetala*
Wild Date Palm: *Phoenix reclinata*
Wild Mango Tree: *Cordyla africana*
White Syringa: *Kirkia acuminata*

xiseketelo xa nonga: wooden pillow or headrest

zenith: the greatest height
zwidzimu: ancestors